GRAPHIC COMMUNICATION

STANDARD GRADE COURSE NOTES

Peter Linton and Mike Wood

Leckie & Leckie

Published by
Leckie & Leckie
8 Whitehill Terrace
St Andrews, Scotland, UK KY16 8RN
tel: 01334 475656 fax: 01334 477392
email: hq@leckieandleckie.co.uk
web: www.leckieandleckie.co.uk

Edited by Neil Stuart

Special thanks to
Bruce Ryan, Hamish Sanderson and Alan Thomson

ISBN 1-898890-61-7

A CIP Catalogue record for this book is available from the British Library.

Printed in Scotland by Inglis Allen.

® Leckie & Leckie is a registered trademark.

Leckie & Leckie Ltd is a division of Granada Learning Limited, part of Granada plc.

Thanks to the following organisations and people for their kind permission to use their photos, drawings and trademarks:

• Strathclyde Passenger Transport (map, page 35)
• Minit UK (instruction card, page 39)
• Humbrol Ltd (assembly instructions, page 39)
• Autodesk, the Autodesk logo and AutoCAD are registered trademarks of Autodesk, Inc. in the USA and/or other countries (screenshots, pages 48, 49 and 71)
• The screenshots of Microsoft Word and Microsoft Excel on page 50 and the clipart on page 54 are reprinted with permission from Microsoft Corporation
• Adobe, the Adobe logo and Adobe Illustrator are either registered trademarks or trademarks of Adobe Systems Incorporated in the United States and/or other countries (screenshot, page 50)
• Land Rover UK (photo, page 54)
• Front cover reproduced from USBORNE BOOK OF FACTS AND LISTS by permission of Usborne Publishing, 83–85 Saffron Hill, London EC1N 8RT, UK. Copyright © 1987 Usborne Publishing Ltd. (page 55)
• Chris Power (2 photos, page 58)
• Dean Wilmot-Lamarche (photo, page 58)
• Pete Frieden (photo, page 58).

Leckie & Leckie Ltd acknowledges all trademarks mentioned in this book. Every effort has been made to trace copyright holders for material used in this book. If any have been inadvertently missed, Leckie & Leckie will be pleased to make the necessary arrangements.

All other names, addresses and other details of companies, people, organisations, products and events are fictitious and are used for illustrative purposes only.

CONTENTS

INTRODUCTION

WHAT IS GRAPHIC COMMUNICATION?

Graphic Communication is a vital part of everyday life. Drawings, sketches and illustrations are forms of graphic communication which we all use.

As **consumers**, we interpret graphs, instruction manuals, adverts, house plans and kitchen designs.

At **work**, designers, architects, illustrators and surveyors produce graphics to be used by builders, engineers, town planners and the general public.

Your Graphic Communication course gives you experience in:
- drawing using instruments and computers
- freehand sketching
- producing illustrations and layouts in colour.

EQUIPMENT

During the course you use drawing equipment, including drawing boards, T-squares or parallel motion, set squares, compasses, pencils and rules.

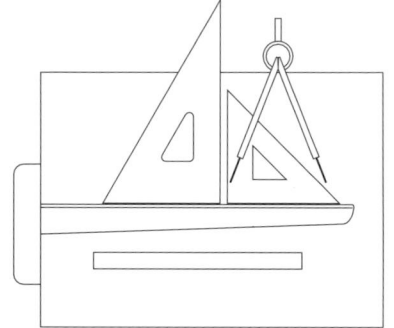

You use computer systems and graphics software and learn how they help in the design and production of modern graphics.

Your portfolio includes coloured illustrations and requires the use of marker pens, bleed-proof paper, chalk pastels and coloured pencils, as well as computer graphics.

Your teacher will demonstrate the use of drawing equipment, computer software and illustration materials. It is important that you work hard to learn how to improve your drawing board and computer skills.

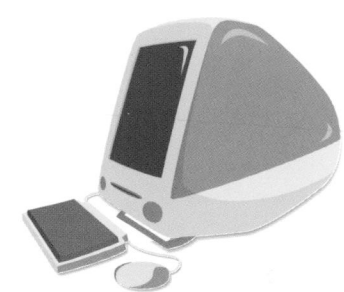

In this book, it is assumed that you are already familiar with this equipment and have gained experience in using it.

THE COURSE

The Graphic Communication course is made up of three elements:
- **Drawing Abilities** (DA)
- **Knowledge and Interpretation** (KI)
- **Illustration and Presentation** (IP).

Each element has equal weighting in your course assessment.

You will be assessed at Foundation, General or Credit level. Your grade will depend on how well you do in each of the three parts. It is hoped that you will aim for Credit level. Even if most of your work falls into Foundation or General levels, you may find it possible to achieve Credit level in some topics. This could make a big difference to your overall grade. You should always attempt each topic to the best of your ability.

It is important to remember that Standard Grade Graphic Communication is a practical course. To be prepared for the course exams, you need to practise each drawing topic many times. Your teacher will provide enough drawings to do (for DA) and questions to answer (for KI) to ensure that you are ready for the course exams.

This book will be your guide through the course. It will help you design and compile your portfolio. Drawing examples will help you understand your class work and prepare you for the drawing exams. The detailed *Knowledge and Interpretation* notes are an ideal reference for class work and revision.

SECTIONS IN THIS BOOK

This book is divided into three sections, covering each element of the course up to Credit level.

Section One: Drawing Abilities

An example of each topic has been drawn in stages. Notes accompany each stage to explain the important points. The examples shown are all of Credit level. Most of these drawings include dimensions so that you can draw them yourself.

Section Two: Knowledge and Interpretation

Each topic is covered in detail. Use this information to help with your class work, homework and exam preparation. Each exam paper will include *Knowledge and Interpretation* questions which require written answers. Homework tasks are included with most of the KI topics covered in this book. You can check your answers to these homework tasks on page 72.

Section Three: Illustration and Presentation

The content of portfolios will vary from school to school. This book shows typical examples of Credit level *Illustration and Presentation*. You should design your own graphics for your portfolio and not simply copy your teacher or the examples in this book. Each item is shown in several stages of production, with notes explaining the important points. More information about the portfolio and its assessment is given on page 51.

(Please note that diagrams and illustrations in this book are not shown to scale.)

PREPARING FOR YOUR EXAM

EXAM PAPERS

There are three exam papers, one at each level: Foundation, General and Credit. You will sit either Foundation and General or General and Credit. Your teacher will discuss this with you after your prelim exams. It is important that you take your teacher's advice about which two papers to sit and that you discuss your choice with your parents.

The duration of each paper is as follows:
- Foundation   1 hr 15 min
- General   1 hr 30 min
- Credit   1 hr 45 min.

The exam papers test your *Drawing Abilities* and *Knowledge and Interpretation* skills. Based on your performance in the exams, you will be awarded a grade in each of these elements. These grades will be combined with your *Illustration and Presentation* (portfolio) grade to determine your overall result in Graphic Communication.

EXAM TOPICS

The topics tested in the exams are all covered in this book. Plan your study in your study planner (a typical study planner is shown below). Study one topic at a time.

		Mon	Tue	Wed	Thur	Fri	Sat
23 April – 29 April	1 hour	Graphic Communication	Mod Studs	Maths	Computing Studies		Art & Design
	1 hour			English			
	1 hour	German			Chemistry		
	1 hour						
30 April – 6 May	1 hour	Computing Studies	Mod Studs	German	Art & Design		Maths
	1 hour		Maths				
	1 hour	English		Graphic Communication	Chemistry		
	1 hour						Graphic Communication

STUDY TIPS

- Start your revision as early as possible in the course. This will help you prepare well and build your confidence.
- Choose a study room which is quiet and comfortable.
- Make sure that all the materials you need, including drawing board and drawing instruments, pencils and paper, are available at your study table.
- Work out the best times of the day for studying.
- Try to study in one hour blocks with breaks between them.
- Plan your study time on your study planner. This saves time and mental energy during the study sessions.
- Drawing practice is very important. If you have a drawing board at home, you can borrow previous exam questions from school. Drawing them again at home is an excellent way to practise.
- Good quality drawing boards can be bought from your local art shop or bookstore. Your teacher may lend you a board and instruments for the duration of the course. It is recommended that you have the use of one at home.
- If you don't have a drawing board at home, you can still do useful study. Take your completed drawings home and follow them through, line by line, from start to finish.
- You can work through the drawing examples in this book on the drawing board or in your head.
- The *Knowledge and Interpretation* section in this book will prepare you for the KI questions in the exam. Read it carefully.

EXAM TECHNIQUE

- Ensure you know the dates, times and places of your exams as far in advance as possible.
- Avoid being late – rushing around will only make you nervous.
- Do only light revision the night before the exam and on exam day. This will keep your mind fresh.
- Organise your exam equipment, e.g. pencils, drawing board and instruments – your teacher may let you set up your desk the day before the exam.
- Read the questions on your exam paper carefully. Rereading them is time well spent.
- Answer easier questions first. Don't get bogged down with difficult questions. Come back to them later.
- Keep your drawings and your written answers neat and tidy.
- Spend time thinking about the question. This can save time when drawing or writing the answer.
- Take all the time given for the exam. Try to leave time at the end to check your answers.
- In written answers, examiners look for quality, not quantity. Make sure you answer what has been asked. Don't just write all you know about each topic.
- Don't rub out your construction lines. This is your 'working'. The examiners will award marks for correct construction methods.

DRAWING CONVENTIONS, SYMBOLS AND BRITISH STANDARDS

INTRODUCTION

Symbols and **conventions** are used in order to simplify the drawing process. They make drawings **simpler** and **quicker** to produce and **easier to understand**. They ensure consistent standards in all types of technical drawings, regardless of who produces them. These symbols are understood by all those involved. This is called **standardisation**.

Two groups of people use technical drawings:
- people who produce drawings: architects, designers and draughtsmen and women
- people who read and work from drawings: engineers, builders, electricians, joiners and manufacturers.

STANDARDISATION

The drawing symbols used in Britain have been standardised by the **British Standards Institution** (**BSI**). At present, the BSI books *PP7308* (Engineering), *PP7307* (Graphical Symbols) and *PP7320* (Construction) are used in British schools. These books describe British and European drawing standards. They will soon be replaced by *BS8888* which will establish worldwide standards for all types of design and drawing. This will lead to consistent standards around the world and will help eliminate confusion between designers, architects and engineers from different countries.

> **MORE INFO**
>
> Symbols devised by the British Standards Institution are used throughout this book. The following pages all contain detailed information about British Standards:
> - page 11 (3rd angle projection symbol)
> - page 21 (dimensioning)
> - page 22 (cross-hatching sectional views)
> - pages 32 to 34 (building drawings and symbols)
> - page 36 (safety signs and public information symbols)
> - page 37 (flow chart symbols)
> - page 38 (electrical symbols)

DRAWING SYMBOLS

The most common drawing symbols are shown below. You will use them in your course work drawings. It is important to understand and remember them. Study their use in the design drawings of the Swallow dart shown on page 7.

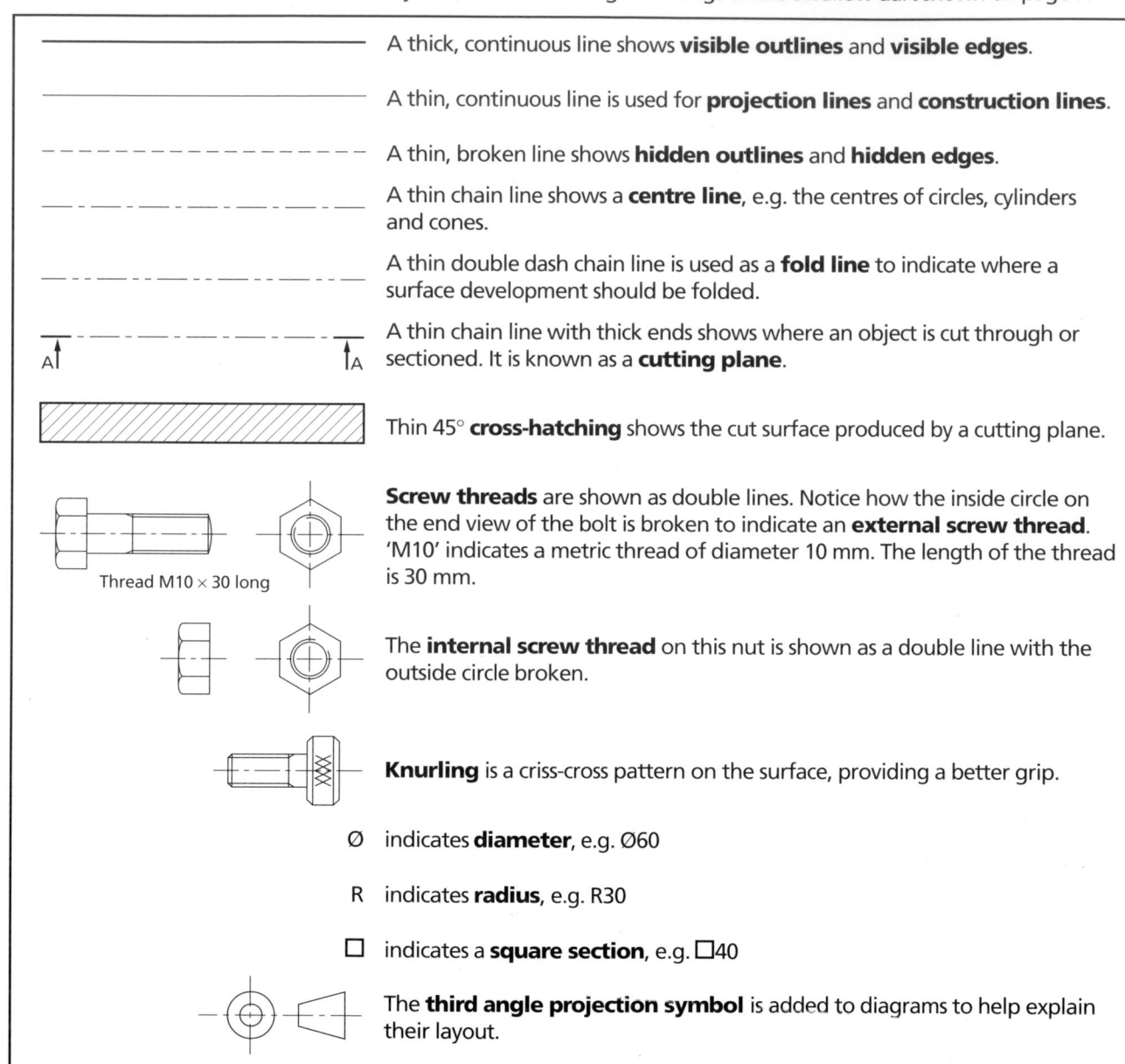

A thick, continuous line shows **visible outlines** and **visible edges**.

A thin, continuous line is used for **projection lines** and **construction lines**.

A thin, broken line shows **hidden outlines** and **hidden edges**.

A thin chain line shows a **centre line**, e.g. the centres of circles, cylinders and cones.

A thin double dash chain line is used as a **fold line** to indicate where a surface development should be folded.

A thin chain line with thick ends shows where an object is cut through or sectioned. It is known as a **cutting plane**.

Thin 45° **cross-hatching** shows the cut surface produced by a cutting plane.

Screw threads are shown as double lines. Notice how the inside circle on the end view of the bolt is broken to indicate an **external screw thread**. 'M10' indicates a metric thread of diameter 10 mm. The length of the thread is 30 mm.

Thread M10 × 30 long

The **internal screw thread** on this nut is shown as a double line with the outside circle broken.

Knurling is a criss-cross pattern on the surface, providing a better grip.

Ø indicates **diameter**, e.g. Ø60

R indicates **radius**, e.g. R30

☐ indicates a **square section**, e.g. ☐40

The **third angle projection symbol** is added to diagrams to help explain their layout.

The Swallow dart design drawings shown here incorporate most of the common symbols described on page 6.

HOMEWORK TASK 1

Study the Swallow dart design drawings and answer the following questions. Refer to the list of drawing symbols on page 6.

1. How many different parts have been assembled to make the complete dart?
2. Which two parts have screw threads?
3. Which part has an external screw thread?
4. What is the diameter of the barrel?
5. How many folds are required to form the flights?

HOMEWORK TASK 2

Study the Swallow dart design drawings and answer the following questions. Refer to the list of drawing symbols on page 6.

1. What type of screw thread is used to assemble the dart and what is the diameter of this screw thread?
2. Which part of the dart has been knurled?
3. Which part of the dart is shown with cross-hatching?
4. Name three types of chain line shown in the drawings.
5. Which drawing shows construction lines?

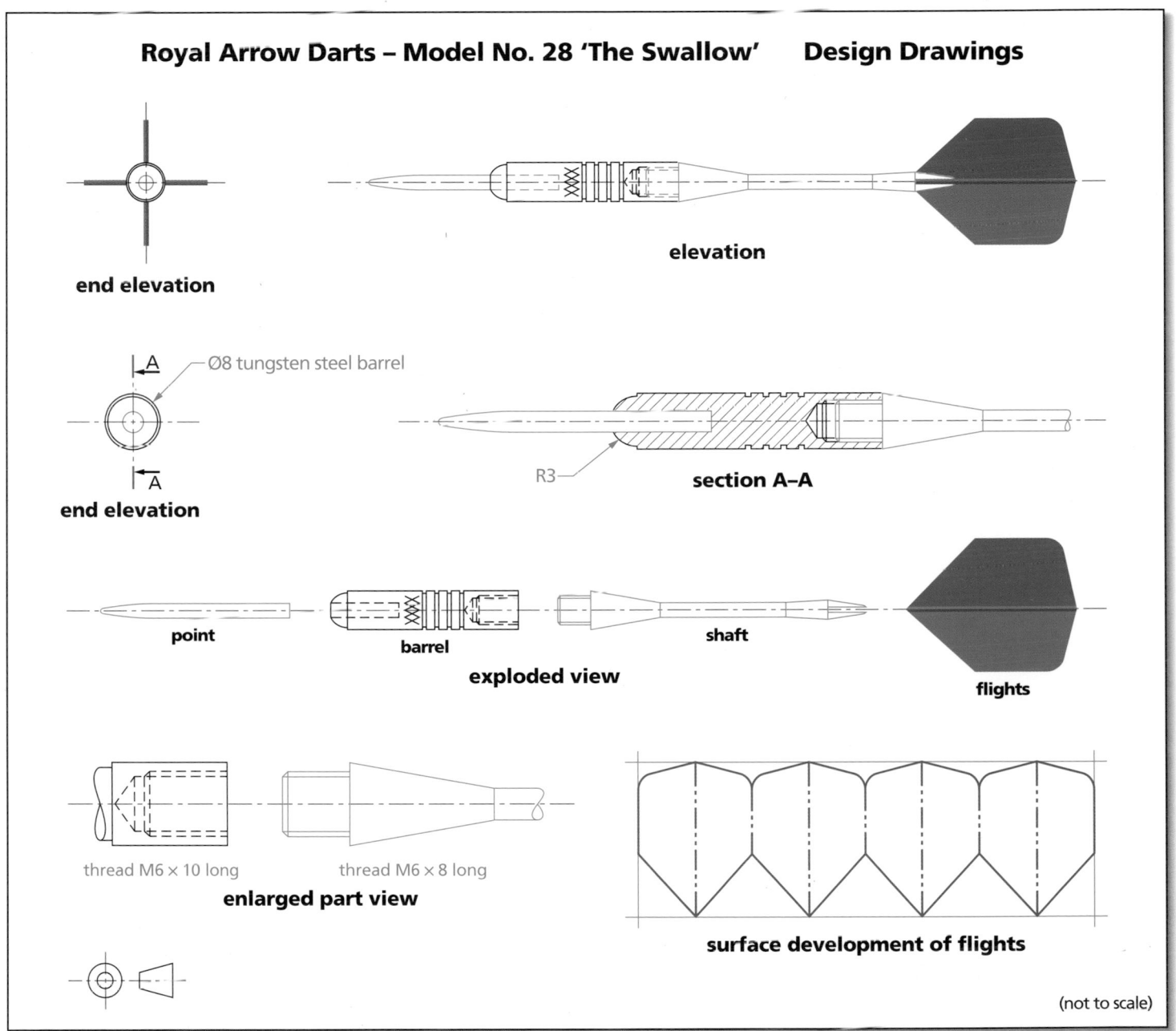

Royal Arrow Darts – Model No. 28 'The Swallow'   **Design Drawings**

end elevation

elevation

Ø8 tungsten steel barrel

R3

section A–A

end elevation

point

barrel

shaft

exploded view

flights

thread M6 × 10 long

thread M6 × 8 long

enlarged part view

surface development of flights

(not to scale)

CIRCLES

Circles form part of many everyday products, and are therefore important when it comes to designing or drawing. You need to understand how to construct and divide circles in order to draw geometric forms such as cylinders and cones.

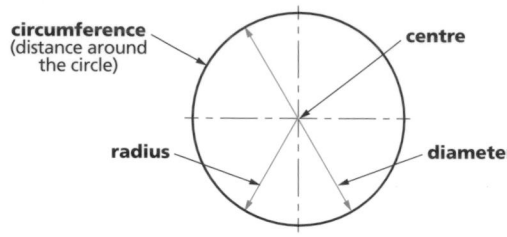

circumference
(distance around the circle)

centre

radius

diameter

This worked example shows how to draw a circle and then divide it into 12 segments. You will do this many times during your course.

1. Draw centre lines.
- Draw two centre lines using your T-square and set square.

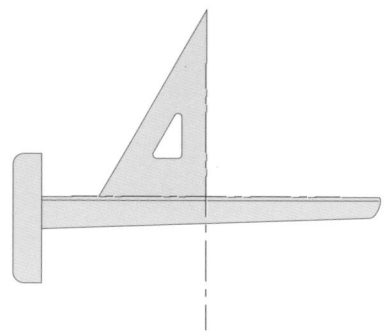

2. Draw the circle.
- Set your compasses to the required radius and draw the circle.

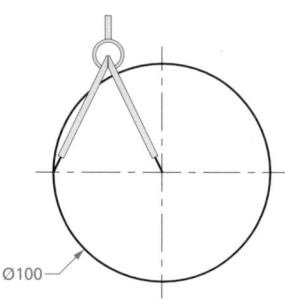

Ø100

3. Divide the circle.
- Divide the circle into 12 by using your 30/60° set square to draw lines, called **generators**, from the centre out to the circle. The angle between each generator is 30°.

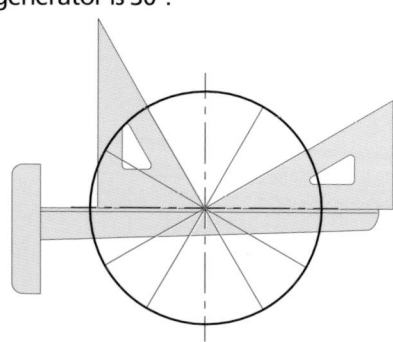

4. Add numbering.
- Number each generator as on a clock face.

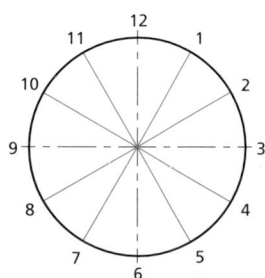

CYLINDERS AND CONES

Generators can be projected along the curved surfaces of **cylinders** and **cones**. These **surface generators** give us reference points on the surface which we can project between views. Generators also help us unfold these forms to produce **surface developments**.

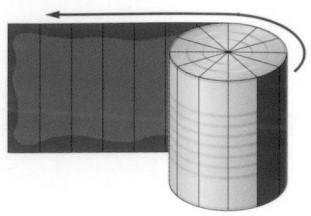

TANGENCY

During your course you will draw objects with rounded corners. A rounded corner is known as an **arc**. The arc blends in with the two straight lines that make the corner. Where a straight line blends into a curve, the straight line is a **tangent** to the curve.

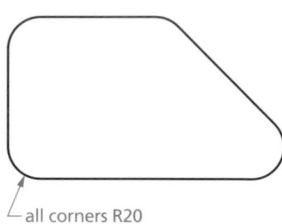

all corners R20

Draw the shape shown here. The stages below show how to find the centre of the corner arcs and draw them. Small arcs, no bigger than R4, are known as fillets – these can be drawn freehand.

1. Draw the outline shape.
- Draw the outline shape using straight lines only.

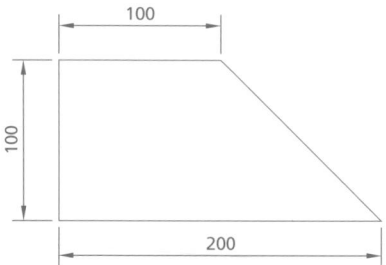

100

100

200

2. Find the centre points.
- Measure 20 mm (the arc radius) in from each edge and draw centre lines. This gives the centre point for each arc.

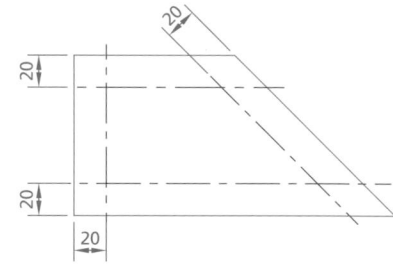

20

20

20

20

3. Draw the corner arcs.
- Set your compasses to R20 and draw curves from the centres. The straight lines should form tangents to the curves.

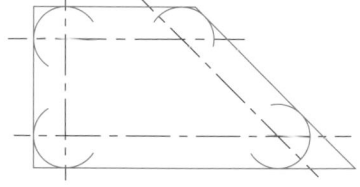

4. Complete the drawing.
- Firm in the outline to complete the drawing.

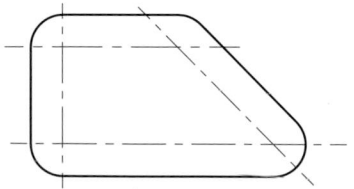

GEOMETRIC SHAPES – ELLIPSES

INTRODUCTION
Ellipses are common geometric shapes. You see an ellipse when a circle is tilted at an angle. There are two main methods of construction: the concentric circle method and the trammel method.

CONCENTRIC CIRCLE METHOD

1. Draw the major and minor axes.
- Draw centre lines to represent the major and minor axes. The long centre line on an ellipse is the major axis. The short centre line is the minor axis.

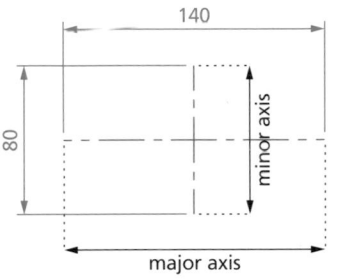

2. Draw the major and minor circles.
- Draw the major and minor circles. Divide them up with 30/60° generators as shown.

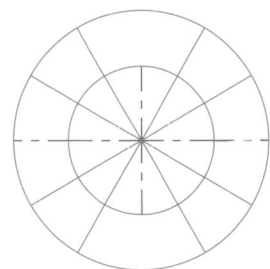

3. Triangulate points.
- Draw horizontal lines where the generators cross the inner circle and vertical lines where they cross the outer circle. Mark the 12 points where these lines cross.

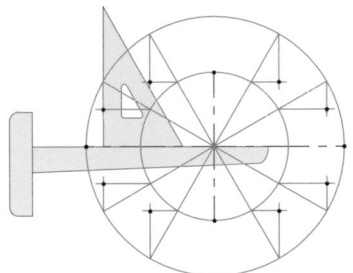

4. Sketch the ellipse.
- Sketch, freehand, the ellipse through the 12 points.

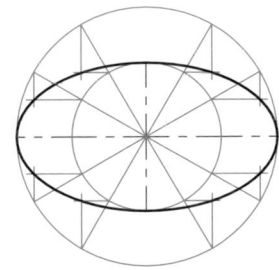

TRAMMEL METHOD

1. Draw the major and minor axes.
- Draw the major and minor axes. Label the centre O, the major axis AA and the minor axis BB.

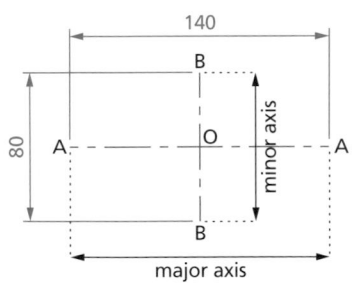

2. Make a trammel card.
- Make a trammel from a strip of card. Draw a mark at one end and call it O.
- Mark the lengths from O to A and O to B on the trammel.

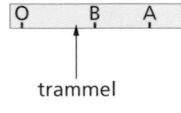

trammel

3. Plot points.
- Line up trammel marks A and B along the axis centre lines and mark a dot beside the mark O. Move the trammel slightly, still keeping A and B on their axes, and mark the next dot. Complete one quarter of the ellipse, then move the trammel around to the next quarter.
- Remember that the ellipse must pass through the end points AA and BB.

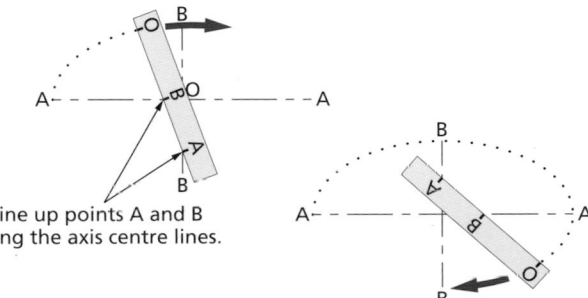

Line up points A and B along the axis centre lines.

4. Sketch the ellipse.
- Sketch in the ellipse through the points.

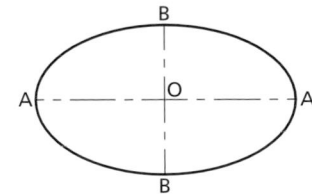

GEOMETRIC SHAPES – HEXAGONS AND OCTAGONS

INTRODUCTION

Hexagons and octagons are common geometric shapes. You need to know how to construct them in order to draw hexagonal and octagonal prisms and pyramids.

HEXAGONS

Two methods are used to construct hexagons: across the corners and across the flats.

ACROSS THE CORNERS

When the size of a hexagon is given **across the corners (A/C)**, you must draw the hexagon **inside** a circle of the same diameter.

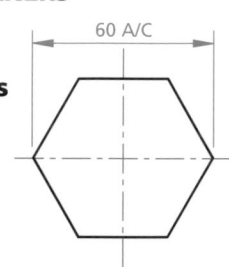

1. Draw a circle.
- Draw a circle to the given diameter, in this case Ø60.
- Divide the circle into 12.
- Draw horizontal lines top and bottom where the generators meet the circle.

2. Draw the hexagon.
- Using a 30/60° set square, draw four sloping lines at 60°.

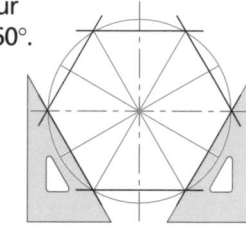

3. Firm in.
- Firm in and tidy up the hexagon.

Note that the hexagon is drawn **inside** the circle. The size across the corners is the same as the diameter of the circle.

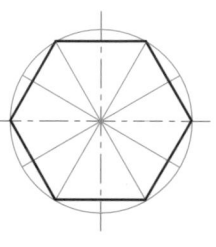

ACROSS THE FLATS

When the size of hexagon is given **across the flats (A/F)**, you must draw the hexagon **outside** a circle of the same diameter.

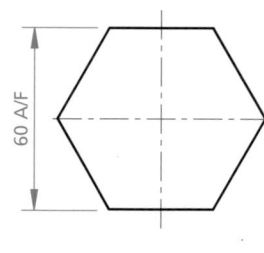

1. Draw a circle.
- Draw a circle to the given diameter, in this case Ø60.
- Draw horizontal lines top and bottom where the centre line meets the circle.

2. Draw the hexagon.
- Draw four sloping lines at 60°, just touching the circle.

When a line blends in with a circle like this, the line is a tangent to the circle.

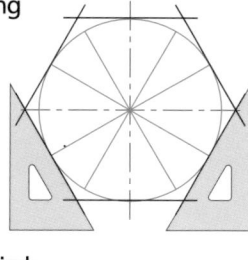

3. Firm in.
- Firm in and tidy up.

Note that the hexagon is drawn **outside** the circle. The size across the flats is the same as the diameter of the circle.

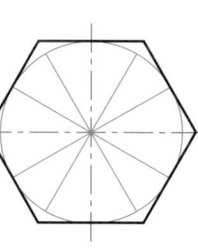

If a hexagon is drawn accurately, all sides are the same length.

OCTAGONS

The size of an octagon is generally given **across the flats** and the octagon is drawn **outside** a circle of the same diameter.

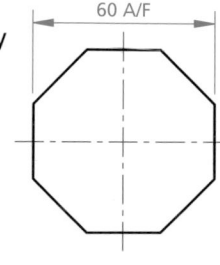

1. Draw a circle.
- Draw a circle to the given diameter, in this case Ø60.
- Add two horizontal and two vertical lines where the centre lines meet the circle.

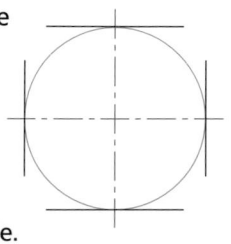

2. Draw the octagon.
- Using a 45° set square, draw four lines which make tangents to the circle.

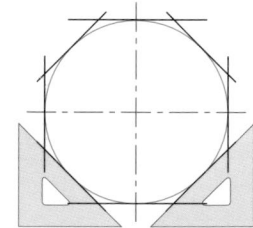

3. Firm in.
- Firm in and tidy up.

All eight sides should be the same length. Check this with your compasses.

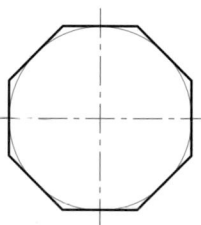

INTRODUCTION

Orthographic projection shows three-dimensional (3-D) objects as two-dimensional (2-D) drawings.

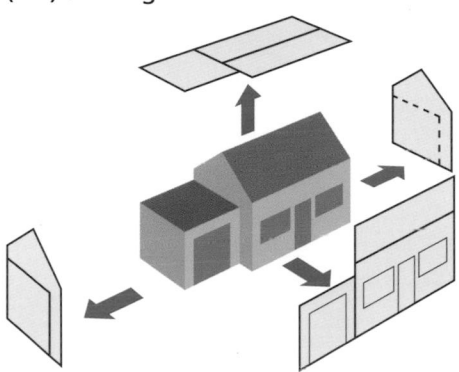

Before a product is manufactured or a building is constructed, accurate detailed drawings must be produced. These drawings are made using orthographic projection systems which are understood around the world.

The most common orthographic projection system is called **third angle projection**.

An object is usually drawn in up to four 2-D views:
• the **elevation**, viewed from the front
• the **plan**, viewed from the top
• two **end elevations**, one from each end.

The views are always set out the same way. Step 4 on this page shows how the four orthographic views are set out. This is the standard layout for all **third angle projections**. Dimensions (lengths, breadths and heights) and other features, e.g. corners and edges, are projected between views.

The third angle projection symbol (right) is added to drawings to help explain their layout.

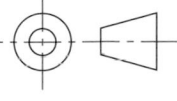

WORKED EXAMPLE

This example shows how to draw and project the four main orthographic views of a house.

1. Draw the elevation.
• Draw a ground line across the page.
• Measure the lengths and heights of the house and draw the elevation above the ground line.

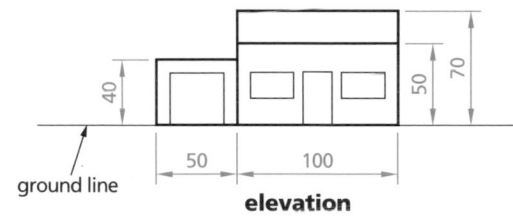

2. Draw the plan.
• Project lines upwards from each corner – this carries the lengths up to the plan. The windows and doors are only flat detail and don't need to be projected.
• Measure the breadths and complete the plan view.

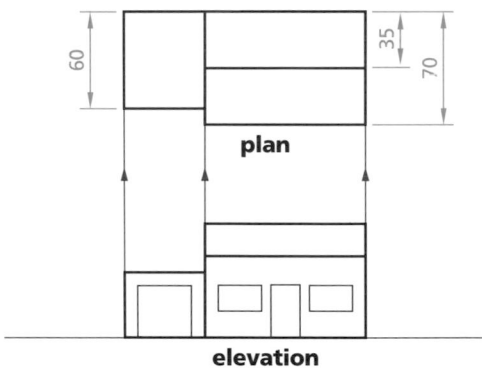

3. Project end elevations using bounce lines.
• Project the heights across from the elevation, ignoring the doors and windows.
• Draw two 45° bounce lines as shown.
• Project the breadths across from the plan.
• Bounce them vertically downward where they meet the bounce lines.

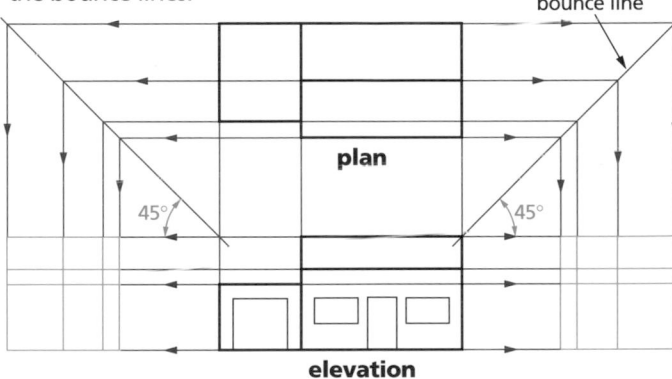

4. Complete the end elevations.
• Follow corners A and B across from the elevation and around from the plan to identify A and B on the end elevations. Each corner can be plotted in this way.
• Number or letter the corners on the elevation and plan. This makes it easier to follow points along the projection lines and on to the end elevations. Put brackets around a label, for example (A), to indicate that the corner is hidden at the back of the object.

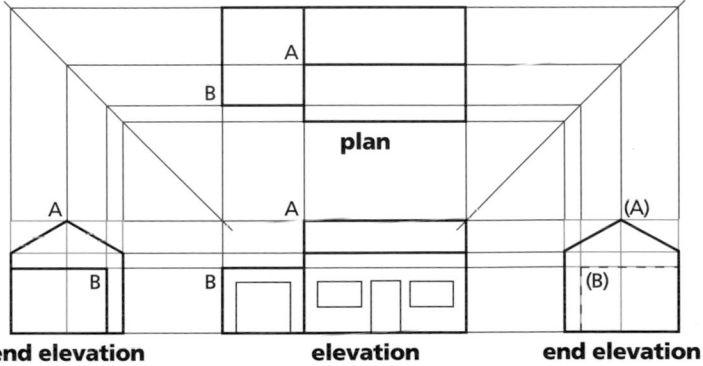

ORTHOGRAPHIC PROJECTION – PRISMS

INTRODUCTION

Prisms are common geometric forms used in packaging and counter displays. There are several different kinds, each taking its name from the shape of its base. During your course you will draw square, rectangular, triangular, hexagonal and octagonal prisms. A hexagonal prism is shown on this page.

WORKED EXAMPLE

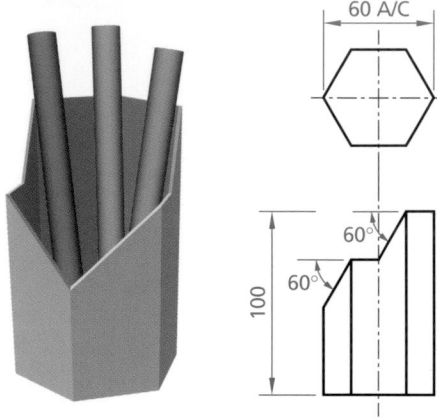

A cardboard box to display pencils is being made in the form of a hexagonal prism. From the information above, draw:
• the plan and elevation
• the end elevation to the left
• the surface development, not including the base.

1. Draw the plan and elevation.

• Draw the plan view first. Use the 'across the corners' method.
• Project down to draw the elevation.
• Number the six vertical edges on plan and elevation.

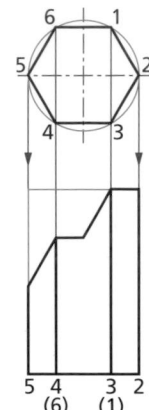

2. Draw the left end elevation.

• Draw a 45° bounce line and project the breadths around from the plan.
• Number the vertical edges.

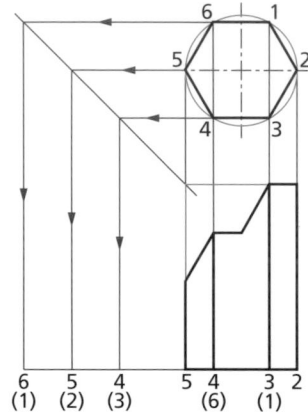

3. Complete the left end elevation.

• Project the heights across from the elevation. Use the numbers to plot the corners on each edge.

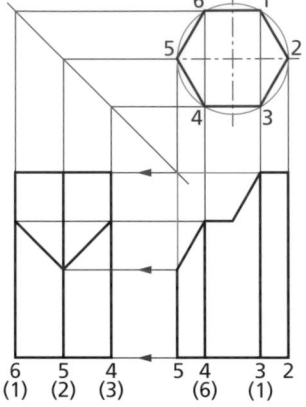

4. Draw the surface development.

• Project the heights along from the elevation.
• Using compasses, step off the length of a side six times.
• Number each vertical fold line starting with the shortest, in this case number 5.

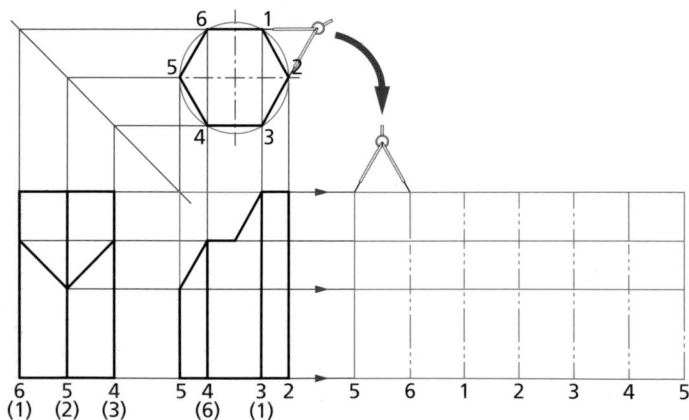

5. Complete the surface development.

• Using the numbers as a guide, plot the top edge of the surface development.
• The corners on the top edge which lie between edges 3 and 4 and edges 1 and 6 need extra construction lines, **a** and **b**, drawn. Using compasses, step the positions of lines a and b from the elevation.
• You may wish to add a glue tab.
• Firm in the outline and add titles.

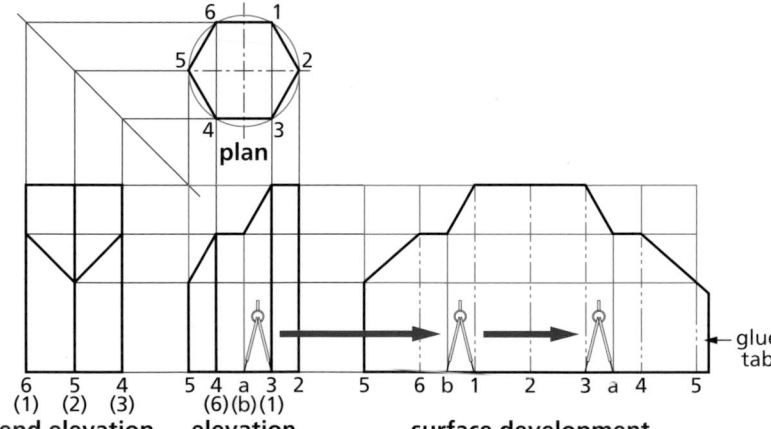

© Leckie & Leckie

ORTHOGRAPHIC PROJECTION – CYLINDERS

WORKED EXAMPLE

The label for a plastic shampoo bottle is to be made for a design mock-up of the bottle. From the information given, draw:
- the plan and elevation
- the left end elevation
- the surface development.

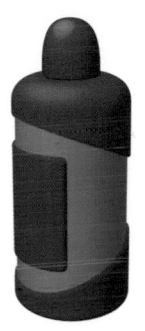

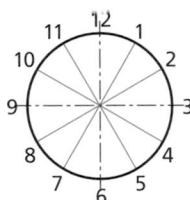

Ø60

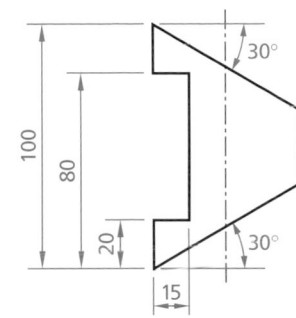

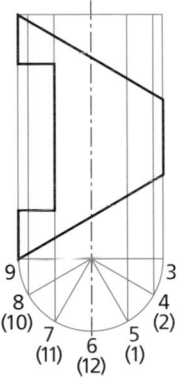

100

80

20

15

30°

30°

1. Draw the plan and elevation.
- Draw the plan and divide it into 12. (Dividing the plan helps you to visualise the drawing.)
- Draw the complete elevation and add surface generators as shown (the blue lines travelling up the elevation).
- Number each surface generator.
- Draw the outline of the label.

In this example, a bounce line is not used. Instead, semicircles are drawn underneath the elevation and end elevation. The semicircles are divided into six and numbered as shown. Surface generators are projected upwards from the semicircle. These numbered surface generators allow you to draw without a bounce line. However, if you prefer, you can use a bounce line instead.

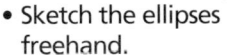

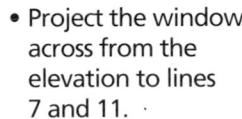

2. Draw the complete end elevation.
- First draw the centre line.
- Then draw the semicircle.
- Divide the semicircle into six and project the generators upwards.
- Number the generators.
- Project the heights across from the elevation and plot the points.
- Sketch the ellipses freehand.
- Project the window across from the elevation to lines 7 and 11.
- Firm in the outline.

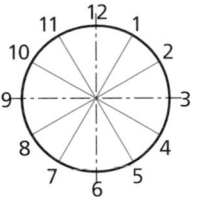

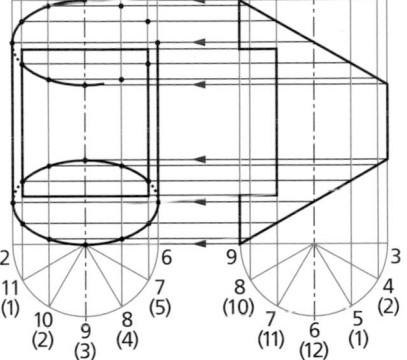

3. Draw the surface development.
- Project the full height across from the elevation.
- Step off the circumference in 12 steps.
- Draw in surface generators.
- Number the generators 1 to 12, starting and ending with the shortest edge.

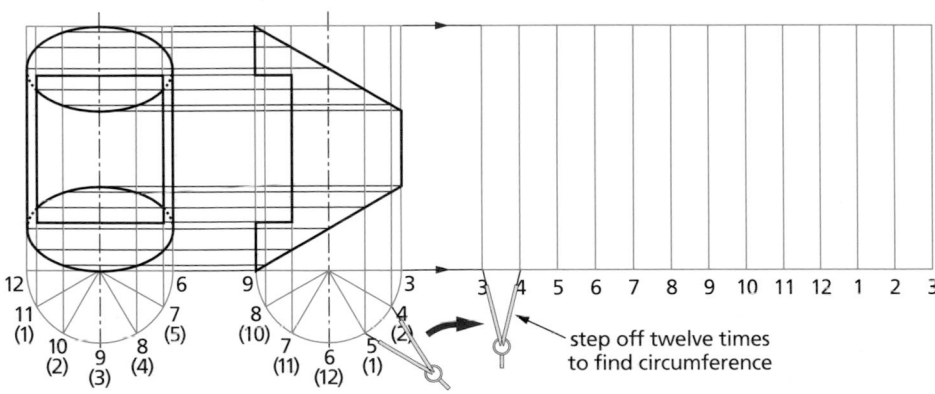

step off twelve times to find circumference

4. Complete the surface development.
- Project heights across from the elevation to complete the top and bottom edges.
- Project the window outline across from the elevation. Remember to use the numbers to plot the correct points.
- Firm in the outline.

plan

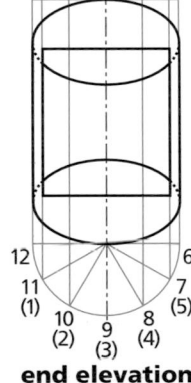

end elevation

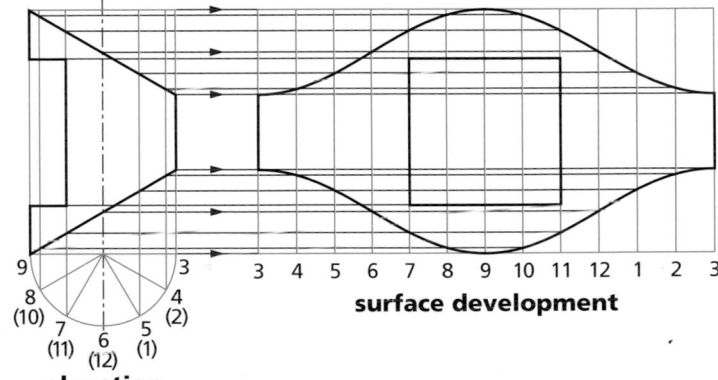

elevation

surface development

ORTHOGRAPHIC PROJECTION – PYRAMIDS AND TRUE SHAPES

WORKED EXAMPLE 1

A child's play tent is to be made in the form of a cut-off square pyramid. Draw:
- the elevation and plan
- the end elevation on the left
- the surface development of the four sides
- the true shape of the top of the tent.

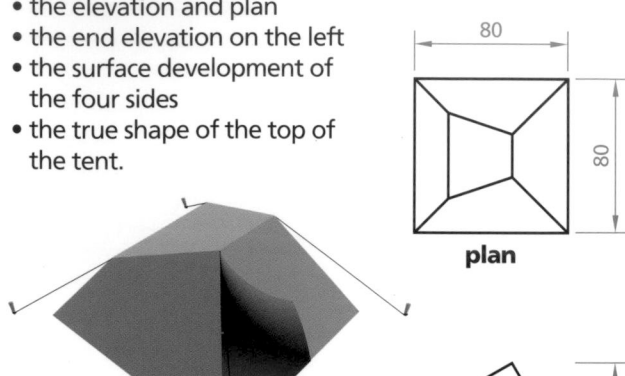

plan

elevation

1. Draw the elevation and plan.
- Draw the elevation, including the apex 'O'.
- Project upwards and draw the plan.
- Number the four corners and the apex.
- Project points a, b, c and d up to the plan.

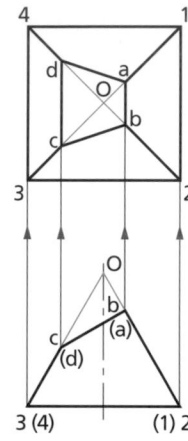

2. Draw the end elevation.
- Project heights across from the elevation.
- Use the bounce line to project breadths from the plan.
- Follow the numbers to plot the shape of the end elevation.

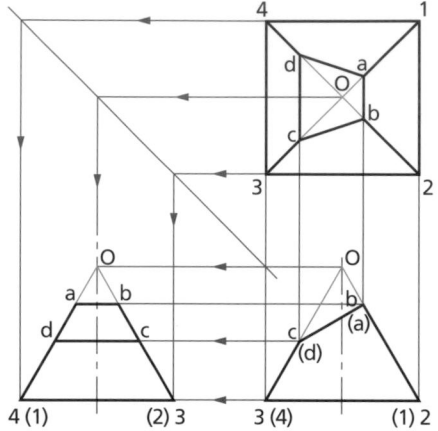

3. Find the true length of a complete edge.
- On the plan, swing edge O–1 around until it is horizontal.
- Drop this point down to the ground line.
- On the elevation, join this new point to the apex O. This **true length** becomes the radius for the surface development.

Swing edge O–1 around until it is horizontal and project it down to the ground line.

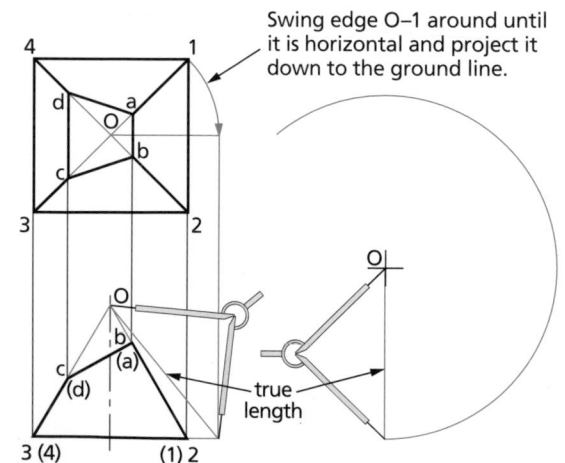

true length

4. Step off the four sides.
- Step the base length around the arc four times.
- Number these points and join them to the centre (point O).

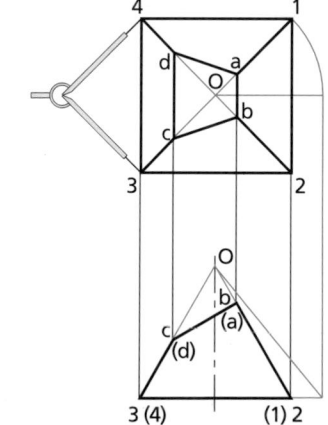

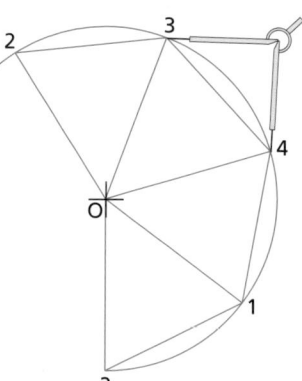

5. Complete the surface development.
- On the elevation, project points a, b, c and d across to the true length.
- Step these sizes onto the surface development.

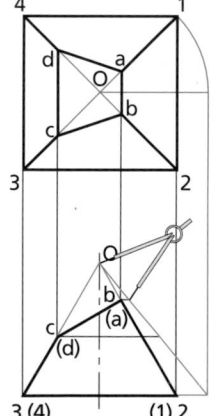

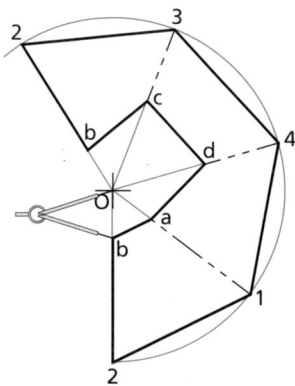

6. Draw the true shape of the top.

- Choose the view which shows the sloping surface as a single line (in this example it is the elevation).
- Project at 90° from this surface (this gives the true length of the surface).
- Draw a **datum line** at 90° to the projection lines. (A datum line is a line from which measurements are taken.)
- Add a horizontal datum line to the plan. This datum line can be anywhere on the plan but it is normal to pass it through the lowest corner of the surface or through the centre of the surface.

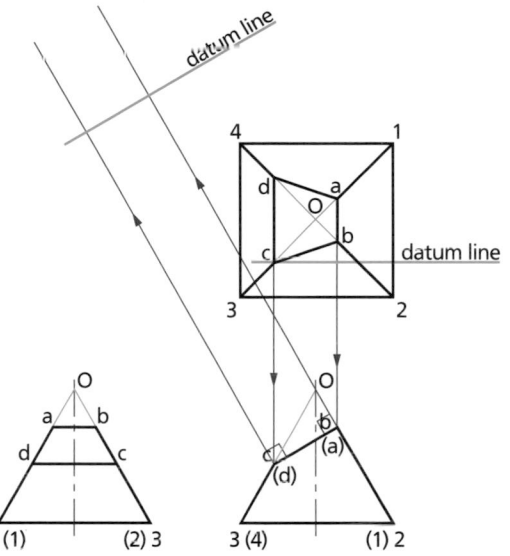

7. Complete the true shape.

- Take the breadths above the datum line on the plan.
- Step them off above the other datum line.
- Mark and label points a, b, c and d.
- Join them to find the true shape of the top surface.

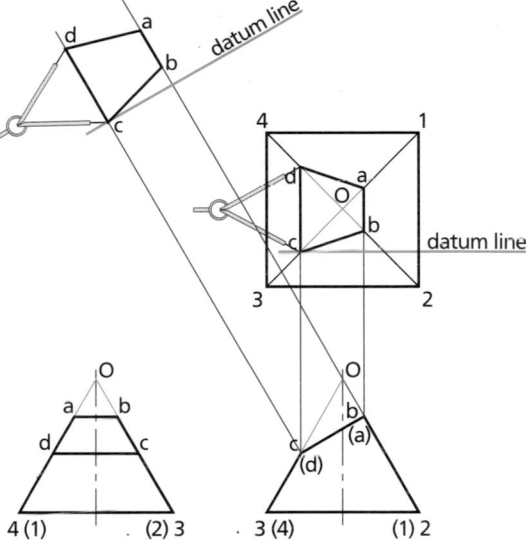

8. The finished drawing.

Here is the complete drawing showing elevation, plan, end elevation, surface development and true shape.

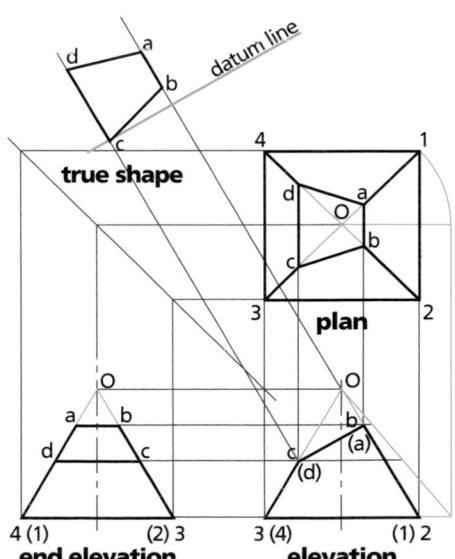

true shape

plan

end elevation   elevation

surface development

WORKED EXAMPLE 2

You can be asked to project true shapes from any straight-sided forms, e.g. pyramids and prisms. This example shows how to project the true shape of a surface of a prism using the centre line as the datum.

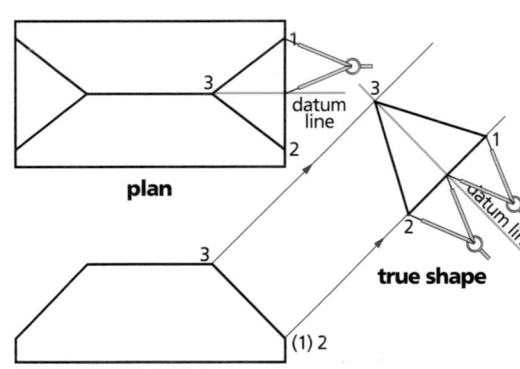

plan

end elevation

elevation

true shape

1. Choose the view which shows the surface as a single line.
2. Project at 90° from the surface.
3. Draw a datum line at 90° to the projection lines.
4. Add a horizontal datum line to the plan. In this example, the datum line passes through the centre of the surface.
5. Take the breadths above the datum line on the plan.
6. Step them off on both sides of the other datum line.
7. Mark and label points 1, 2 and 3.
8. Join them to find the true shape of the sloping surface.

WORKED EXAMPLE

An air-bed foot pump in the form of a cut-off cone is being designed. Drawings are required so that graphics can be planned. From the elevation given, draw:

- the plan view
- the end elevation on the right
- the surface development
- the true shape of this sloping surface.

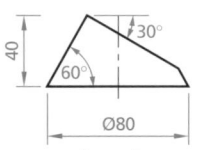

elevation

1. Draw the elevation, plan and end elevation.

- Complete the elevation of the cone.
- Divide it into 12 using surface generators.
- Number each generator.
- Draw a complete plan and end elevation.
- Split each into 12 using surface generators. Be careful to ensure the views are numbered correctly.

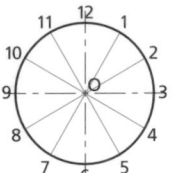
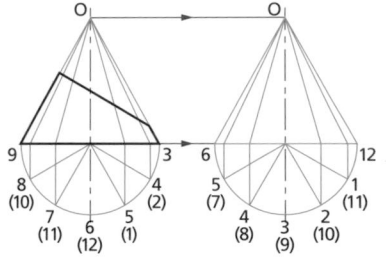

2. Complete the plan and end elevation.

- Where each generator crosses the sloping surface, project across to the end elevation. Mark each point on the end elevation. Use the numbers on both views to check the points are correct.
- Project up from the elevation to the plan. Mark each point.
- The points on generators 6 and 12 need to be stepped off with compasses as shown.
- Sketch in the curves on the end elevation and plan.

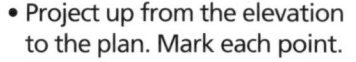
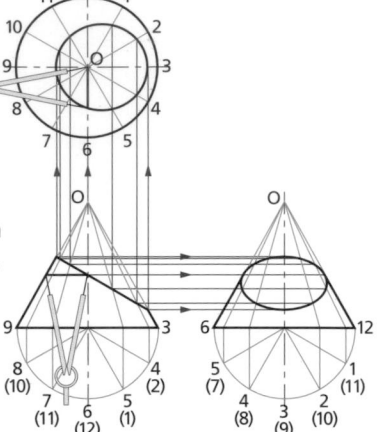

3. Draw the surface development.

- Take the true length of the surface generators (down the outside of the elevation, lines 3 or 9).
- Draw an arc using this true length.
- Take the distance between generators at the base and step it off 12 times around the arc.
- Number these points and join them to the apex, O. Start numbering using the shortest generator, in this case number 3.

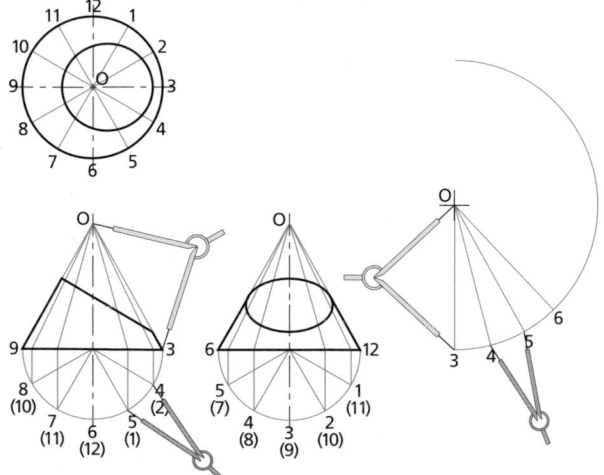

4. Complete the surface development.

- On the elevation, project across from the slope to the true length line. This finds the true length of each point from the apex to the slope.
- Take these sizes from the true length line and step them on generators around the surface development. Work from the apex, O, each time. Use the numbers to avoid mistakes.
- Sketch in the curve.

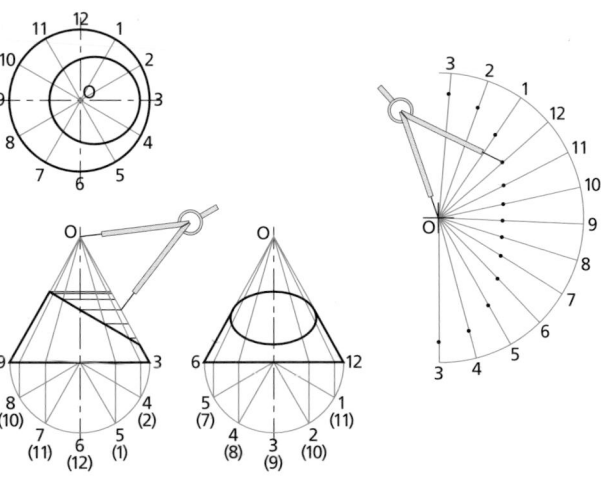

5. Draw the true shape of the sloping surface.

(Refer back to page 15 for the procedure for projecting true shapes.)

- Find the view which shows the surface as a straight line.
- Project each point at 90° to this line.
- Add a datum line at 90° to the projection lines.
- Go back to the plan to pick up the breadths.
- Step the breadths to both sides of the datum line.
- Sketch the curve neatly.

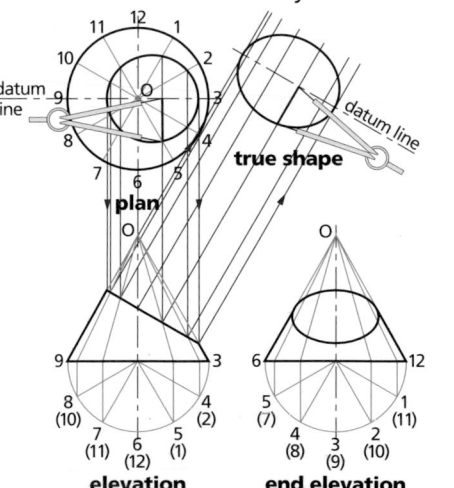
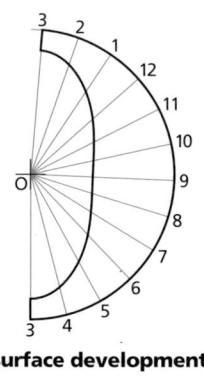

surface development

PICTORIAL DRAWING – CABINET OBLIQUE

INTRODUCTION
Pictorial drawings look 3-D, as opposed to orthographic drawings which look 2-D.

Cabinet oblique drawing is a simple form of pictorial drawing which is often used when it is important to show the **front view** of an object.

RULES OF CABINET OBLIQUE DRAWING
- The front of an object is shown as its **true shape**.
- **Breadths** are projected back at **45°**.
- If the sides are drawn to their true breadths, then the drawing looks unrealistic. To make the drawing look more realistic, all **breadths** are cut to **half actual size**.

WORKED EXAMPLE
Two views of a camera are shown on the right. Using instruments and starting at corner X, draw an oblique view of the camera.

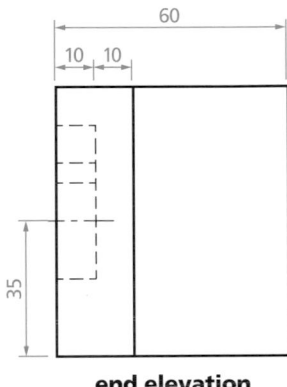

elevation

end elevation

1. Draw the front.
- Draw the front view of the camera as seen on the elevation.
- Oblique lines are projected back at an angle of **45°** **from the front view**. You should also draw one from the centre of the lens.
- Draw the inside edge of the lens. Make sure that the centre of the circle is positioned at the correct distance (half depth), 5 mm, from the original centre.

Note that any circle drawn on the front of the oblique drawing is a **true circle** and can be drawn using compasses.

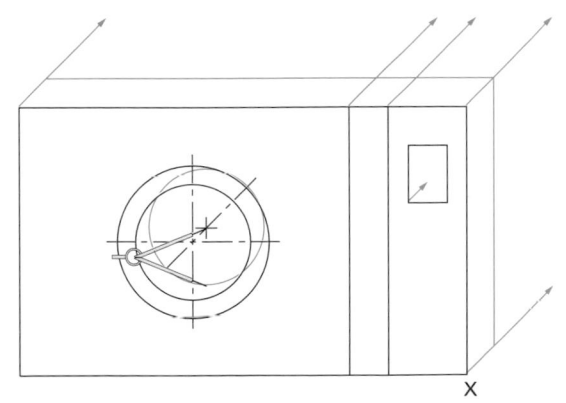

2. Add breadths.
- Measure and mark off the **half-breadths** on each projection line.
- Lightly draw in the back edges.
- Trim the circle to show the lens detail.
- Similarly, trim the viewfinder detail.

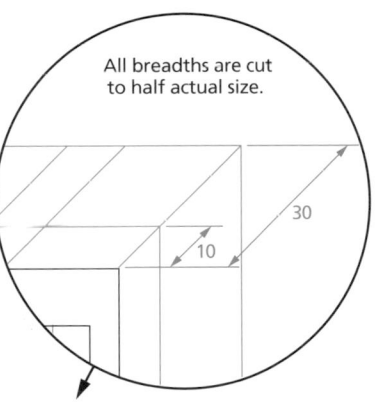

All breadths are cut to half actual size.

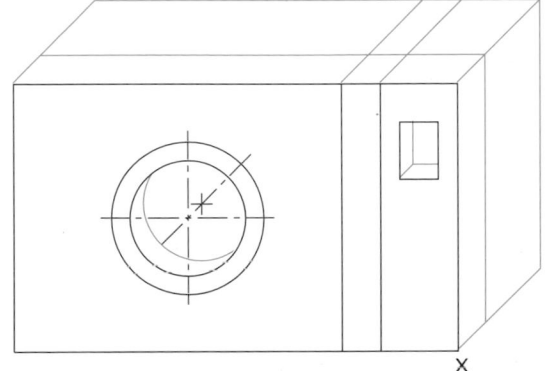

3. Firm in.
- Remove any extra construction lines.
- Firm in the drawing.
- Add title.

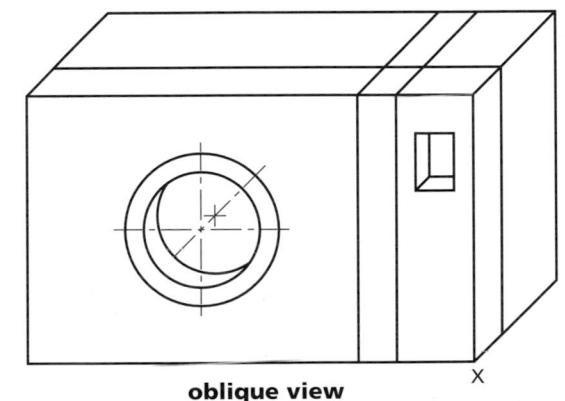

oblique view

PICTORIAL DRAWING – ISOMETRIC

INTRODUCTION

Isometric drawing is a method of pictorial drawing where all three dimensions and three surfaces are shown in one view. Isometric means **'having equal measure'**. You can produce an isometric drawing more easily by constructing an **isometric crate** first. You can then draw the object inside the crate.

RULES OF ISOMETRIC PROJECTION

• Heights are projected vertically upwards.
• Lengths and breadths are projected at 30° to the horizontal.
• All measurements along the height, length and breadth are full size.

HOW TO CONSTRUCT AN ISOMETRIC CRATE

1. Draw the vertical axis.

• Draw in the vertical edge and mark off the overall height.

height (120 mm)

90°

2. Draw the isometric axes.

• Project the 30° lines from the base of the vertical line using a 30/60° set square.

height

length (120 mm)

breadth (50 mm)

30°   30°

3. Add dimensions.

• Measure and mark off the overall length and breadth.
• Draw in remaining verticals and 30° lines to produce a crate (box).

This is an empty crate. Use this process to construct crates to contain isometric views of objects or buildings.

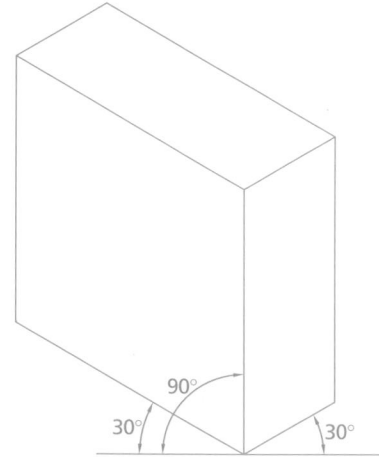

90°

30°   30°

HOW TO DRAW AN ISOMETRIC CIRCLE

1. Slice up the circle and isometric crate.

• Draw the elevation and end elevation of a cylinder. Slice it up equally as shown.
• Draw an isometric crate the same size as the circle and add centre lines.
• Slice up the front of the isometric crate the same as the elevation.
• Transfer sizes directly from the front elevation onto the corresponding numbered slice on the isometric crate.

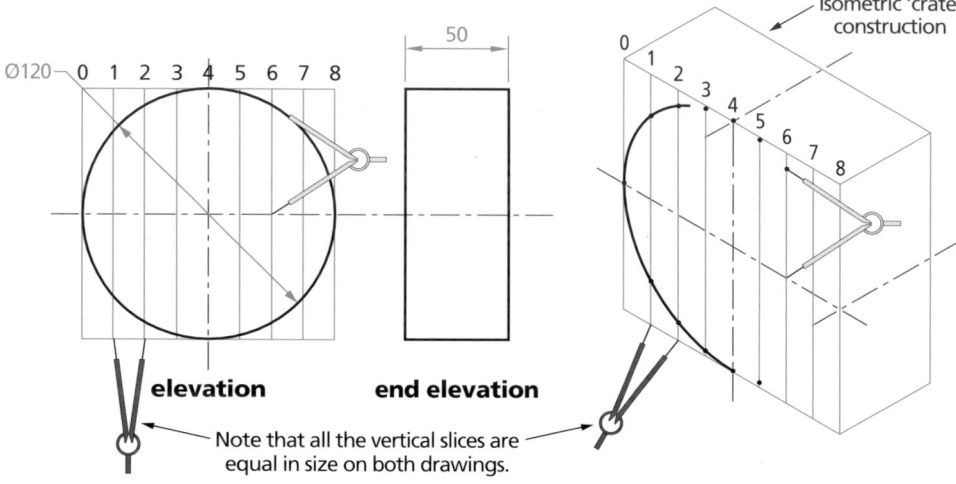

Isometric 'crate' construction

50

Ø120   0 1 2 3 4 5 6 7 8

0 1 2 3 4 5 6 7 8

elevation   **end elevation**

Note that all the vertical slices are equal in size on both drawings.

2. Add breadths.

• Project each point on the isometric circle back at 30°.
• Transfer the breadth from the end elevation to the isometric view using compasses.

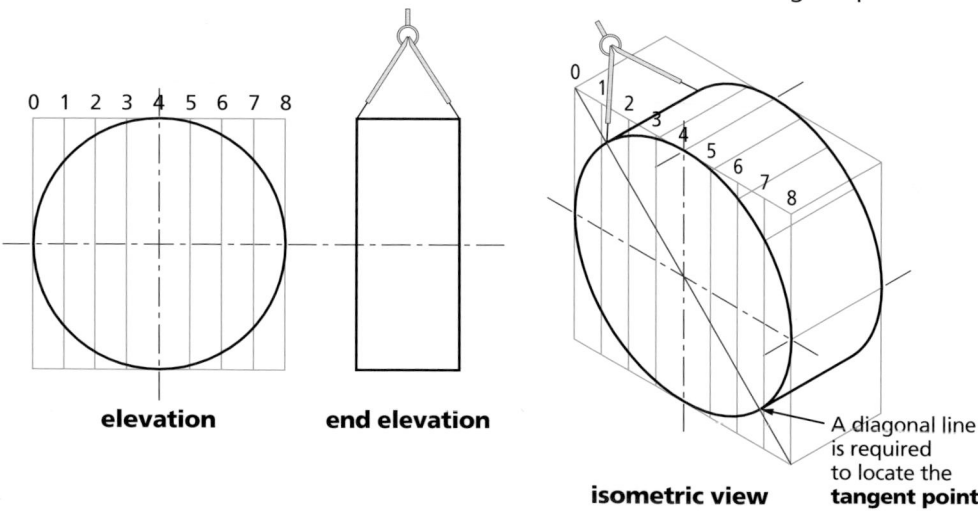

0 1 2 3 4 5 6 7 8

0 1 2 3 4 5 6 7 8

elevation   **end elevation**

A diagonal line is required to locate the **tangent points**.

isometric view

WORKED EXAMPLE

A small mantle clock is shown below. From the information given, draw, to a scale of 1:1, an isometric view of the clock starting with the lowest point indicated at X. Do not draw any hidden detail.

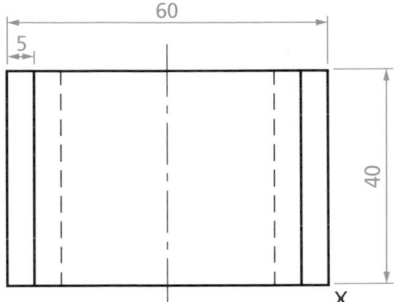

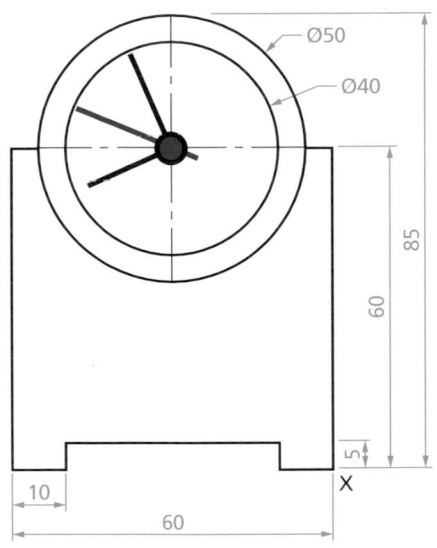

1. Draw the elevation and plan and construct a crate.

- Draw the elevation and plan to the sizes given.
- Draw the isometric crate using the length, breadth and height of the clock.
- The scale is 1:1 so the sizes can be lifted directly from the orthographic views using compasses.
- Identify corner X in the crate.

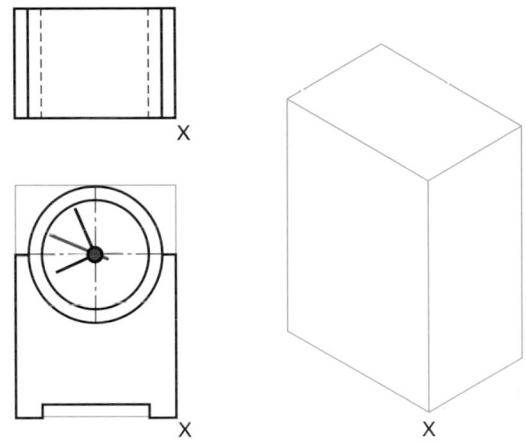

2. Slice up the fronts.

- Divide up the elevation into equal-width slices.
- Transfer the slices to the front face of the isometric view.
- Number the slices accordingly.
- Use compasses to step off the heights for each slice and transfer them to the isometric crate.
- Firm in the profile of the front face.

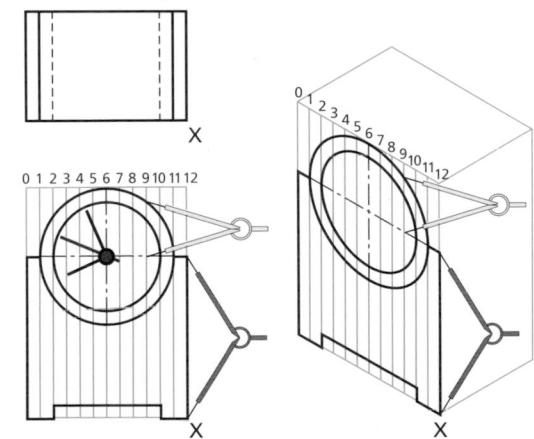

3. Project the breadths.

- Project the breadths back at 30° from each point on the front of the crate.
- Use compasses to transfer the breadths from the plan view to the isometric view.
- Project back at 30° from the tangent point and step off the breadth along this line.

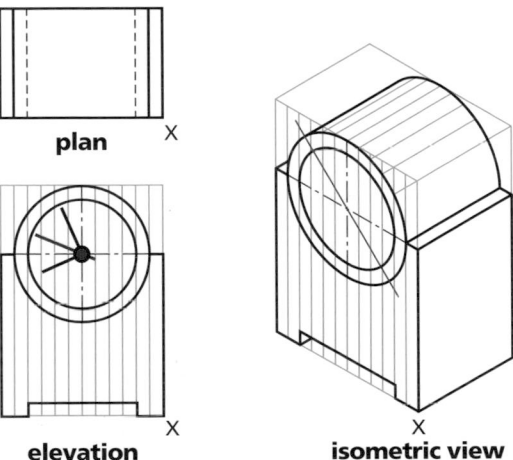

4. Firm in.

- Complete the outline of the clock.
- Add titles to your drawing.

(Remember, do not add hidden detail unless you are asked to.)

plan

elevation

isometric view

PICTORIAL DRAWING – PLANOMETRIC

INTRODUCTION

Planometric projection is a form of pictorial drawing favoured by architects and interior designers. It can be simple to construct and gives a clearer picture of interior spaces than an isometric drawing. A planometric drawing shows the object(s) as if the viewer was hovering above the room or building.

RULES OF PLANOMETRIC PROJECTION

- The base is a true plan view rotated at an angle to the horizontal, usually 30°, 45°, or 60°.
- All vertical edges remain vertical and project upwards from the base.
- All measurements on the base are true.
- Vertical measurements (heights) should be full size.

WORKED EXAMPLE

Two views of a fireplace and TV corner unit for a doll's house are shown on the right. Draw a planometric view of this corner of the living-room, to show the fireplace and the corner unit. Do not show any hidden detail.

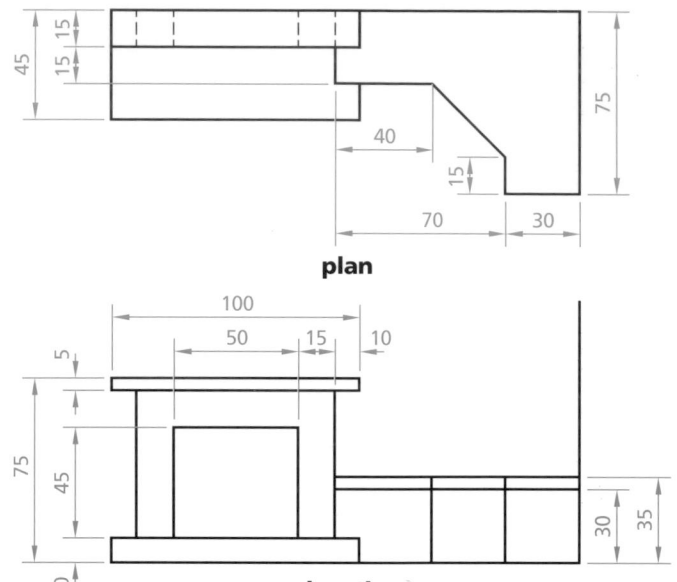

plan

elevation

1. Draw the rotated plan.

- Redraw the plan view of the room rotated at 45°. This provides you with location points (corners) from which to project your heights.
- Letter or number the corners to avoid confusion when marking off the heights.

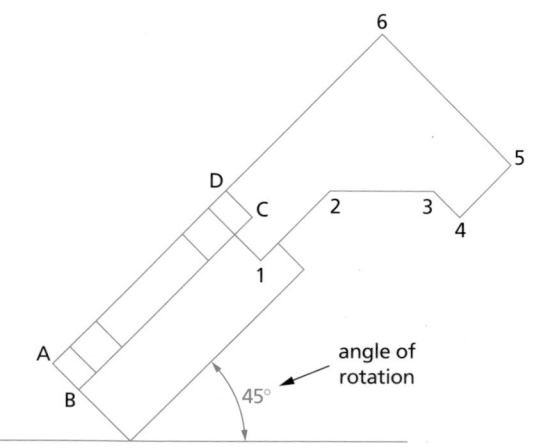

2. Add heights.

- Project construction lines vertically from each corner on the rotated plan view.
- Transfer heights (full size) from the elevation to the planometric view.
- Join up the top edges lightly. Use a 45° set square to project the top lines around the drawing.

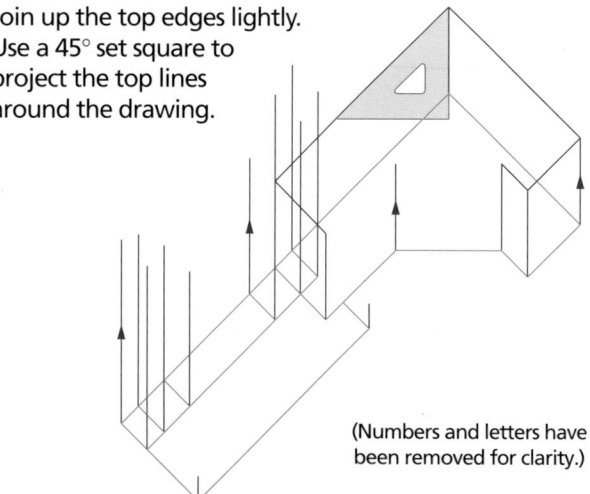

(Numbers and letters have been removed for clarity.)

3. Firm in.

- Firm in outlines of separate parts.
- Remove construction lines.

planometric view

DIMENSIONING

INTRODUCTION

Dimensions (measurements) are essential on most production drawings since they enable the engineer or builder to manufacture products and construct buildings accurately. The dimensioning system used in Britain is set by the British Standards Institution in the book *PP7308* (see page 6).

You will be required to show dimensions on drawings in your IP portfolio and in the course exams. Learn the conventions and rules of dimensioning shown on this page and practise them on your coursework drawings in school.

In most engineering drawings the millimetre is the basic unit of measurement. However, where larger sizes are required, such as in site plans for houses, the metre is the basic unit.

DIMENSIONING RULES

- Each dimension should be shown on the drawing only once.
- Place the dimensions on your drawing so that they can be read from either the bottom or the right-hand side.
- Always measure in millimetres unless instructed otherwise.
- Figures should not touch outlines, dimension lines or centre lines.
- Ø before a dimension denotes the diameter of a circle. R denotes radius.
- On circles, always dimension the diameter, never the radius.
- On curves, arcs and rounded corners, always show the radius.

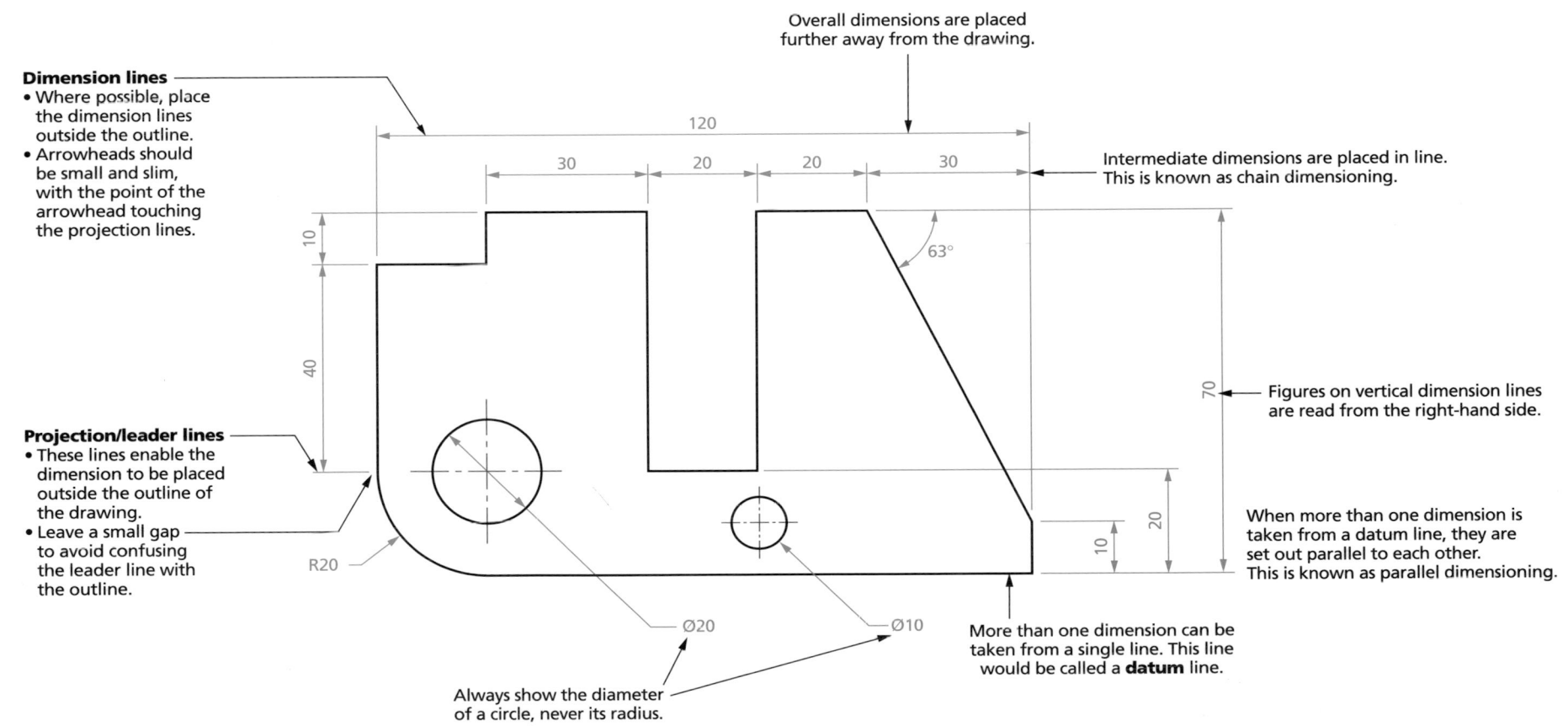

© Leckie & Leckie

SECTIONAL VIEWS – BASICS

INTRODUCTION

Sectional views are used on drawings to show the inside details of an object more clearly than hidden detail can. Sectional views show the internal construction details which may not be obvious from a normal drawing or sketch.

Examples of sectional drawings can be found in workshop manuals and other forms of technical illustration. Sales brochures and promotional posters also make use of sectional views.

CUTTING PLANES

A chain line with thick ends is used to show where the object is sliced through. This line is known as a **cutting plane**. It has arrows to indicate the direction of viewing and letters to distinguish it from other cutting planes.

In the drawing on the right, the cutting plane shows where the object is sliced. The direction of viewing is indicated by the arrows.

SECTIONAL VIEW

The part of the object **behind** the arrows is removed and the sectional view is left. Some hidden edges become visible, so they are drawn as outlines.

CROSS-HATCHING

The section is cross-hatched at **45°**, with the lines approximately **5 mm** apart. The sectioned view is titled according to the cutting plane, i.e. **section A–A**.

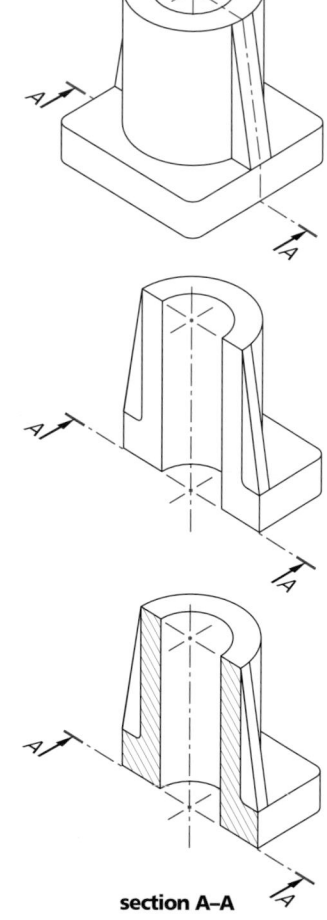

section A–A

WHEN NOT TO HATCH

Various rules apply to sectional views:

- **Webs** (**ribs**) are used to strengthen or support various engineering components. Webs should not be cross-hatched when they are sectioned lengthways.

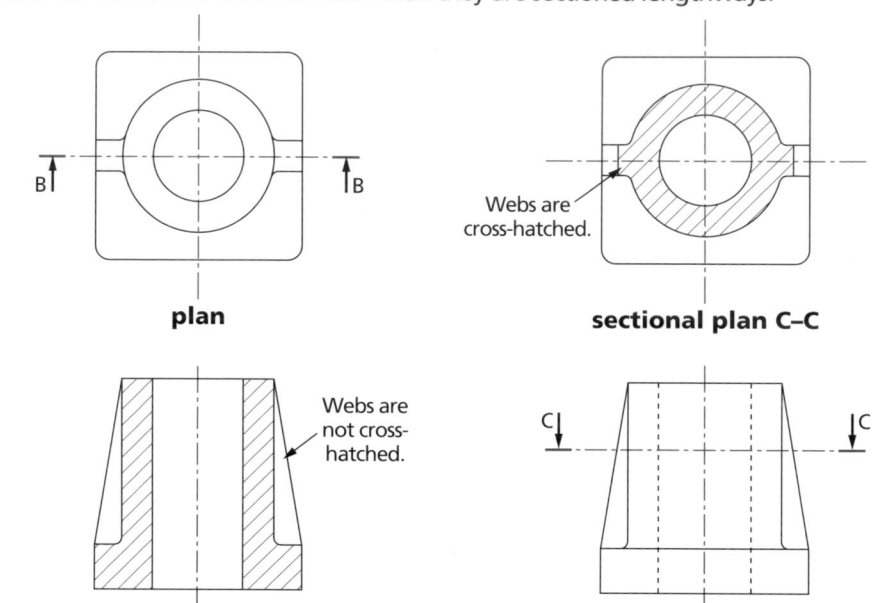

plan

sectional plan C–C

Webs are cross-hatched.

Webs are not cross-hatched.

sectional elevation B–B

elevation

Sectional elevation B–B demonstrates that you **do not** cross-hatch a web that is sectioned **along** its length.

Sectional plan C–C shows that you **do** cross-hatch a web that is sectioned **across** its length.

- Drawing conventions also state that you do not show sections through **nuts**, **bolts**, **washers**, **screws** or **shafts** (**axles**) (see pages 23 and 25).

HIDDEN DETAIL

Do not show hidden detail on a sectional view. For example, in sectional elevation B–B the upper back edge of the base is not shown.

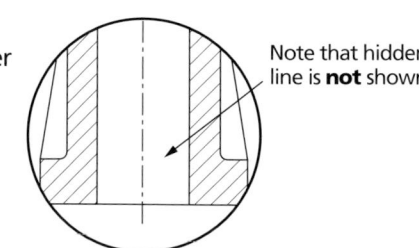

Note that hidden line is **not** shown.

WORKED EXAMPLE

The plan, elevation and an isometric view of a toy engine are shown below. Draw, full size from the given views, the section A–A through the smoke stack. Do not show hidden detail.

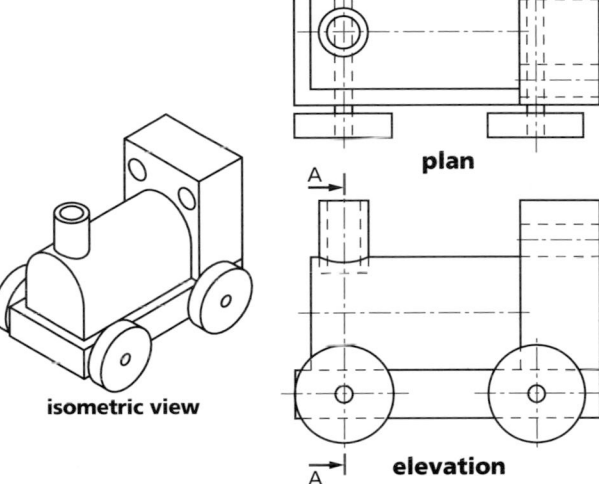

isometric view

plan

elevation

1. Draw projection lines.

- Using a 45° bounce line, project and locate centre lines.
- Project edges from the two given views to the end elevation.

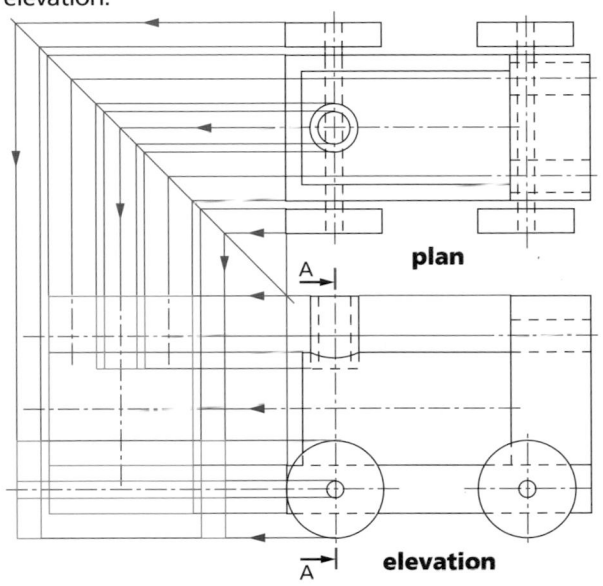

plan

elevation

2. Draw the outlines of each part.

- Lightly outline each part.

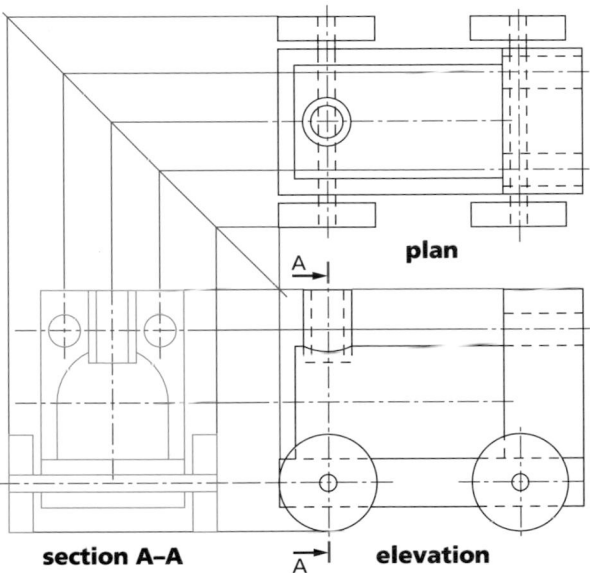

plan

section A–A   **elevation**

3. Add cross-hatching.

- Identify the areas that have been cut through by cutting plane A–A.
- Add cross-hatching to those parts cut by cutting plane A–A.
- Areas that are adjacent to each other should be cross-hatched in different directions.
- Do not cross-hatch the axle. *PP7308* advises that axles, nuts, washers, bolts and shafts should not be cross-hatched.
- Firm in the drawing.

plan

section A–A   **elevation**

> **TIP**
>
> To identify areas to cross-hatch, imagine you are sawing along cutting plane A–A. Which areas would show saw marks after the cut? The inside of the funnel is not cross-hatched – why?

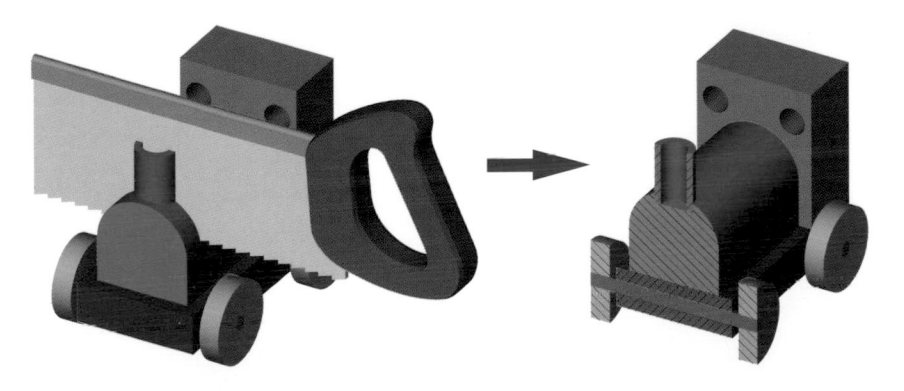

> **TIP**
>
> To draw this sectional end elevation yourself, copy the elevation and plan views at a scale of 2:1, i.e. twice full size. Then project the sectional end elevation as shown.

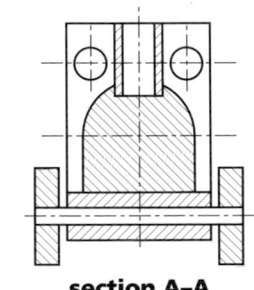

SECTIONAL VIEWS – PICTORIAL

INTRODUCTION

Pictorial drawings (e.g. isometric, oblique and planometric) can be sectioned to show the inside of a product. The product may consist of several parts (**components**). A drawing that shows the assembled product is called an **assembly drawing** (see page 25).

Pictorial assembly drawings can be made using any common pictorial drawing method: isometric, oblique or planometric. Sectioned pictorial drawings are commonly found in:
• maintenance manuals for cars, washing machines and power tools
• DIY flatpack furniture assembly instructions
• plastic model kits and construction toys.

During your course you will draw sectional views of pictorial assemblies. Make sure you are proficient at pictorial drawing before you attempt a sectioned assembly drawing.

WORKED EXAMPLE

Two views of a small plastic trinket box are given (right). An exploded elevation shows the three component parts: base, body and lid. Using instruments, draw an isometric view of the assembly, sectioned through cutting plane **A–A**. Do not show hidden detail.

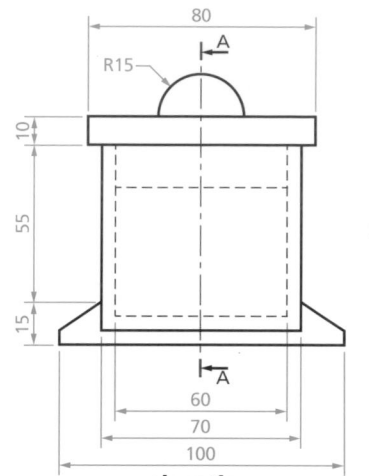

elevation

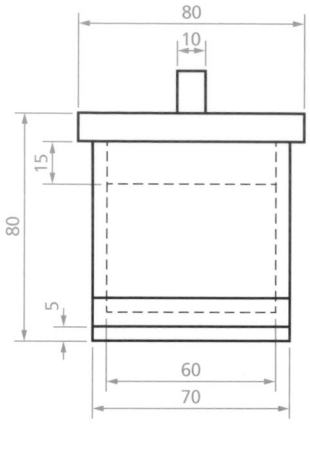

end elevation

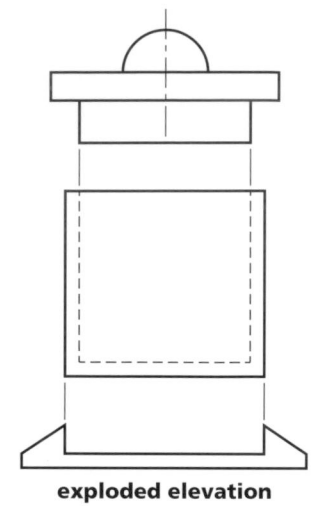

exploded elevation

1. Draw the base.
• Draw a crate for the entire base.
• Construct the base inside the crate.
• Section the base through cutting plane **A–A**.
• Project upwards from the four inside corners to position the body.

2. Draw the body.
• Draw a crate for the entire body.
• Add the wall thickness.
• Section the body through cutting plane **A–A**.

3. Draw the lid.
• Draw the lid insert (the part that fits inside the body). Work outwards from the insert to draw the lid overhang.
• Draw a crate for the handle.
• Draw the handle: draw a circle the same size and take measurements from this to construct the isometric curves (see page 18).
• Section the lid through cutting plane **A–A**.

4. Cross-hatch the drawing.
• Firm in the outlines.
• Show hatching lines on each part. Remember, cross-hatching on adjacent parts should be staggered and run in opposite directions.
• Add title.

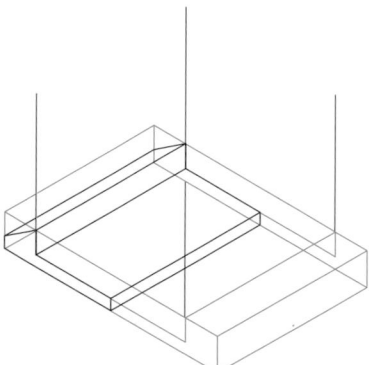

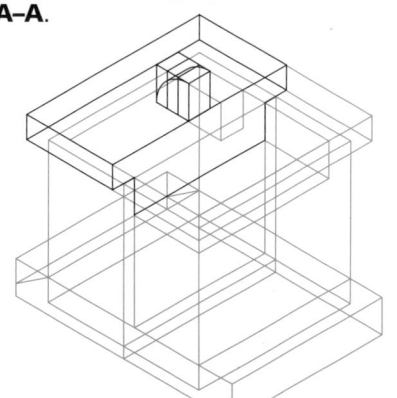

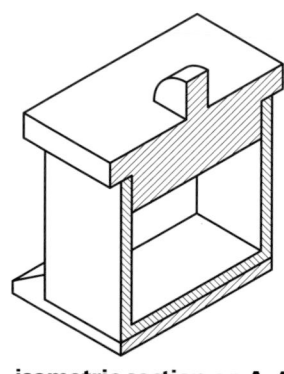

isometric section on A–A

ASSEMBLY DRAWING

INTRODUCTION

Many of the products you draw are likely to consist of more than one part. These parts are called **components**. The type of drawing which shows all the components assembled together is called an **assembly drawing**.

The worked example on this page shows how to build up an orthographic assembly drawing of a trolley castor and section it through the cutting plane X–X.

WORKED EXAMPLE

Details of the component parts of a trolley castor are shown on the right. Draw section X–X of the assembled parts. The axle has been given on the answer sheet.

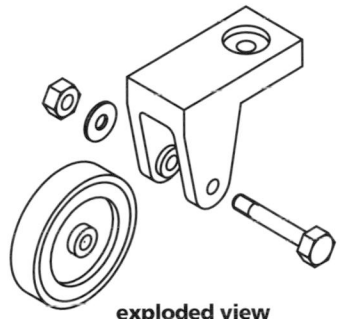

exploded view

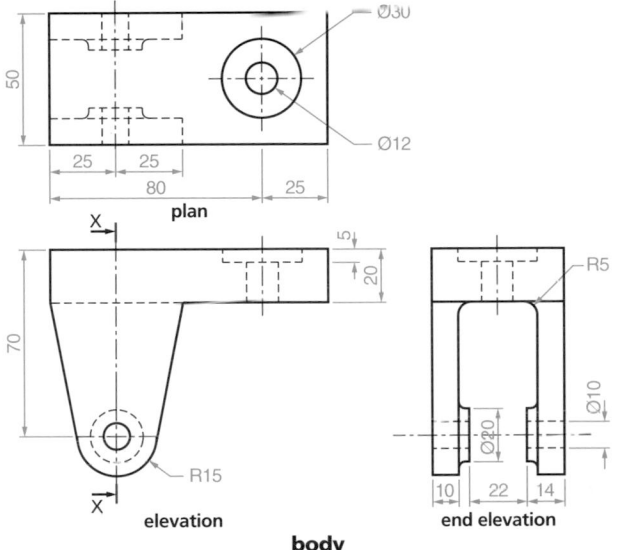

plan

elevation

body

end elevation

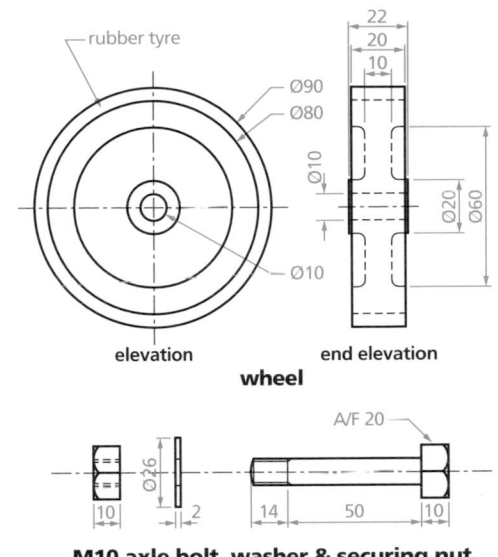

wheel

M10 axle bolt, washer & securing nut

1. Start the assembly.

- A starting point is usually provided on assembly drawings. In this example, the nut and axle bolt assembly is given. The rest of the drawing is constructed around this.

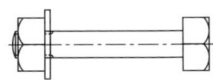

- Look for cutting plane X–X. This is where the assembly is sliced through.
- The arrows indicate the direction of viewing. In this case, all the parts to the left of the cutting plane are removed.
- Section X–X is a sectional end elevation of the assembled parts.

If you are doing this drawing in class, you will have to draw the nut and bolt assembly yourself. Your teacher can help you with this.

2. Draw the body.

- Construct the outline of the body around the bolt. Remember, do **not** draw any hidden detail.
- The exploded view indicates that the M10 axle bolt fits through the Ø10 holes in the body.
- Take your measurements from the centre line through the bolt.

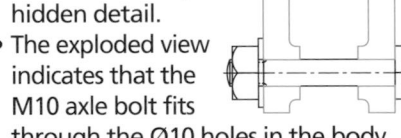

3. Draw the wheel.

- The wheel is 22 mm wide and fits snugly inside the body space.
- Draw the wheel in position. Remember to show the sectioned rubber tyre at the top and bottom.

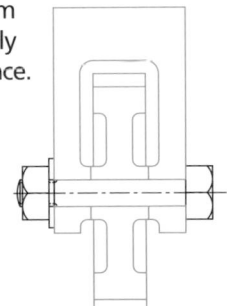

4. Cross-hatch the drawing.

- Outline the profiles of each component. Do **not** show any hidden detail.
- Show hatching lines on body, wheel and tyre. Cross-hatching on adjacent parts should be staggered and run in opposite directions.
- Add title.

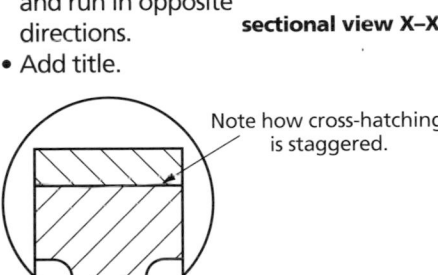

sectional view X–X

Note how cross-hatching is staggered.

TIPS

- An assembly drawing question normally shows you all the parts with dimensions.
- Look for clues as to how the parts can be assembled. Holes often require some other part to fit into them. Screw threads fit together and matching dimensions on different parts may suggest how to assemble the pieces.
- A pictorial sketch is often provided to help you understand how the parts are assembled.
- Make good use of this information to establish a picture in your mind of how the parts fit together and how to start the drawing of the assembled parts.
- You may be asked to draw a sectional view of the assembled parts.

EXPLODED VIEWS – ORTHOGRAPHIC

INTRODUCTION

An exploded view shows the separate parts that make up an assembly. The parts are spaced out so that each part can be seen clearly. The parts are also arranged 'in line'. This helps to show how they fit together. Exploded views are often used to give instructions to people who need to assemble a product.

Good examples of exploded views can often be found in:
• car or machine maintenance manuals
• DIY assembly instructions
• children's construction kits.

WORKED EXAMPLE

An isometric view and two orthographic views of a small plastic trinket box are shown on the right. The box is made up of three parts: a base, a body and a lid. Using instruments, draw an exploded elevation of the trinket box.

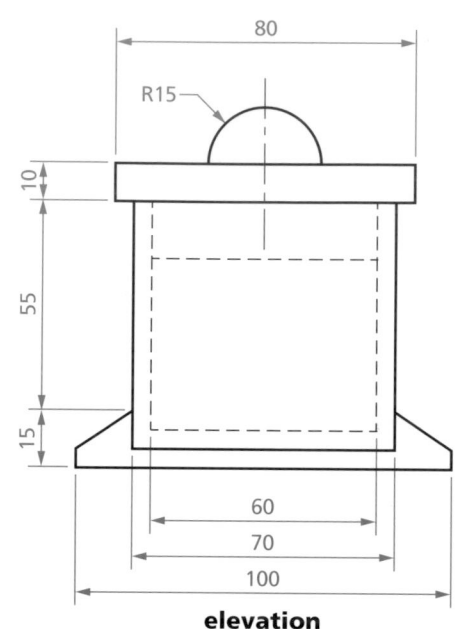

elevation

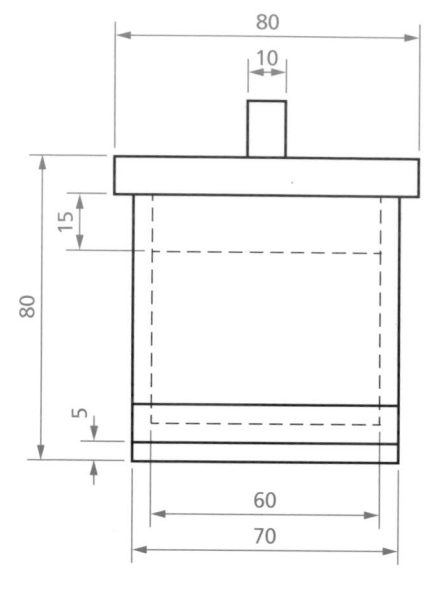

end elevation

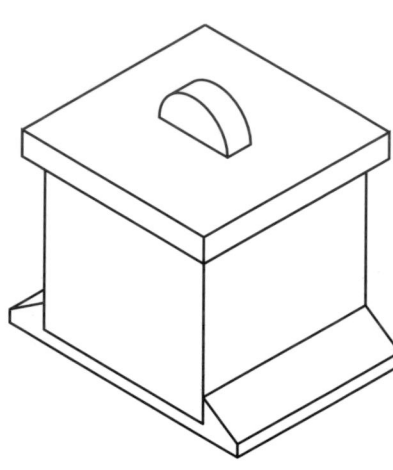

isometric view

1. Choose a starting point.
• Draw the base of the box in position.
• Project inner edges of the base to align with the body of the trinket box.

TIP

Choose your starting point carefully. In this example, we are working from the base upwards.

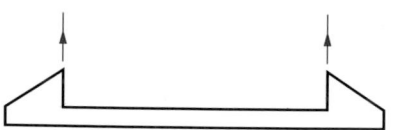

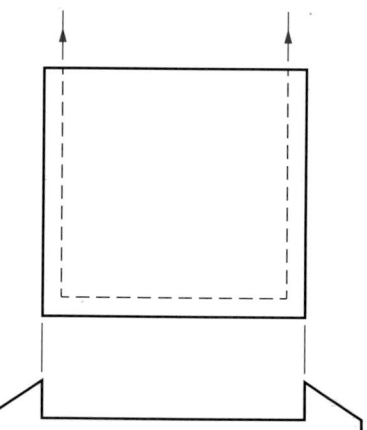

2. Project upwards.
• Draw the body of the box between the projection lines.
• Project the inner edges of the box to align the lid insert.

3. Add the lid.
• Draw the centre line for the semicircular handle.
• Draw the lid in position.

It is important that all the parts are lined up correctly and spaced neatly on the sheet.

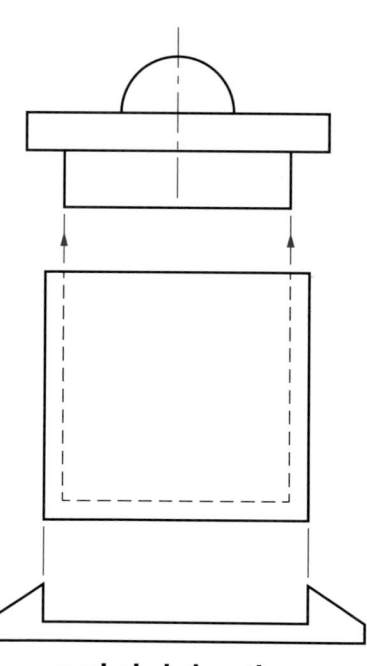

exploded elevation

EXPLODED VIEWS – PICTORIAL

INTRODUCTION

Pictorial drawings can be used to show exploded views of a product. In a pictorial view, the component parts are separated and positioned 'in line'. This gives a clear view of each part and shows how the parts fit together to make an assembly.

Exploded pictorial drawings can be made using any common pictorial drawing method, including isometric, oblique and planometric. Make sure you are proficient at pictorial drawing before you attempt an exploded drawing.

Exploded pictorial drawings are commonly found in:
• maintenance manuals for cars, washing machines and power tools
• DIY flatpack furniture assembly instructions
• plastic model kits and construction toys.

WORKED EXAMPLE

Two views of a small plastic trinket box are shown on the right. An exploded elevation shows the three component parts: base, body and lid. Using instruments, draw an exploded isometric view of the trinket box to show clearly the three component parts. Do not show hidden detail.

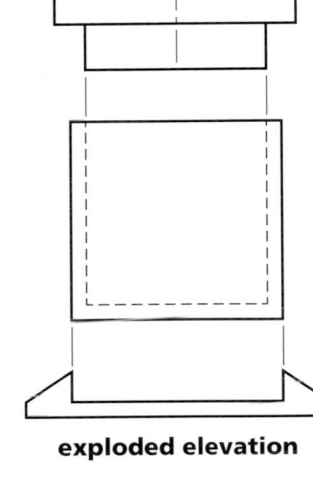

elevation   **end elevation**   **exploded elevation**

1. Draw the base.
• Draw a crate for the base.
• Draw the base inside the crate.
• Project upwards from the four inner corners to position the body.

TIPS
• Note the use of projection lines and crates to align the components for assembly.
• Hidden detail is not required.
• If there is sufficent room, try to leave clear space between the exploded parts.

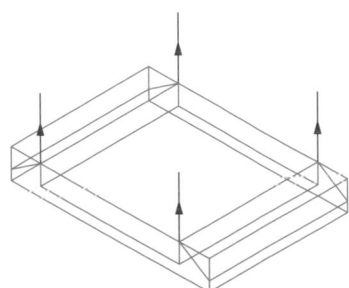

2. Draw the body.
• Draw a crate for the body within the projection lines.
• Add the wall thickness.
• Project upwards from the four inner corners to position the lid.

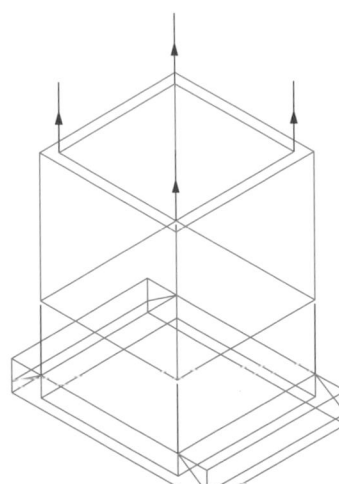

3. Draw the lid.
• Draw a crate for the lid insert within the four projection lines.
• Draw a crate for the lid.
• Draw a crate for the handle.

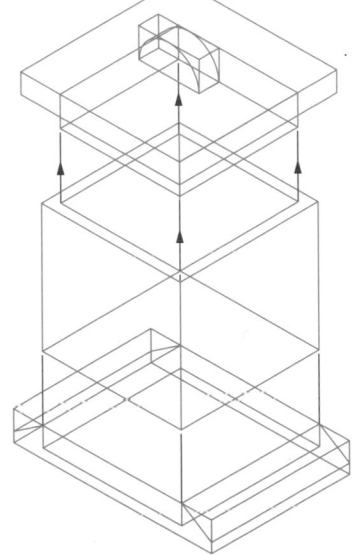

4. Add detail.
• Construct the isometric curves on the handle (see page 18).
• Firm in outlines on all parts.

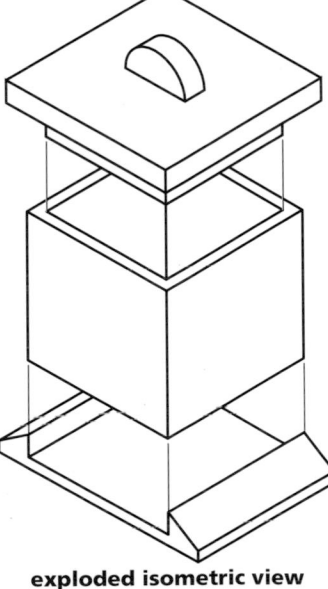

exploded isometric view

SKETCHING TECHNIQUES – BASICS

INTRODUCTION

Sketching is a way of producing graphics quickly. Sketches should be produced freehand, without using drawing instruments. Use a soft (B or 2B) pencil for sketching. It is very important to keep the pencil sharp.

FIND YOUR OWN SKETCHING ANGLE

With a sheet of paper laid square in front of you like a table mat, sketch a series of sloping lines.

- Hold the pencil comfortably.
- Sketch from the bottom up and away from you. If you are left-handed, sketch in the opposite direction.
- Sketch each line in one movement.

This finds your most comfortable sketching angle. From now on you should turn the paper to sketch all straight lines at this angle.

USE BOXES TO BUILD SKETCHES

All sketches, no matter how complex, are built up using boxes. Your first task is to become good at sketching boxes.

- Turn the paper so you can sketch all lines at your most comfortable sketching angle.
- Keep the box lines parallel to the edges of the paper.
- Concentrate on keeping all angles at 90°.
- Keep the lines straight and light.

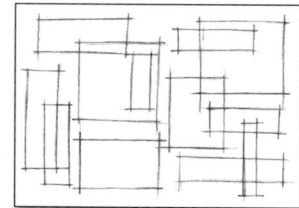

KNOW THE IMPORTANCE OF PROPORTION

Creating the correct proportions is essential. You must train your eye to recognise good proportion. Constructing your sketch in boxes makes this much easier. Try sketches with straight lines first – buildings are ideal. Sketch your own house or school building.

1. Sketch the boxes.

- Box in the elevation. Take great care to get the proportions right.
- Divide it into its main parts.

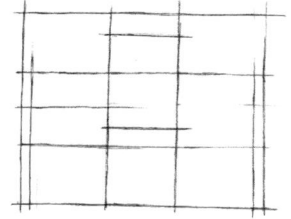

2. Add detail and end elevation.

- Add details and sloping lines.
- Project the heights across and construct the end elevation.

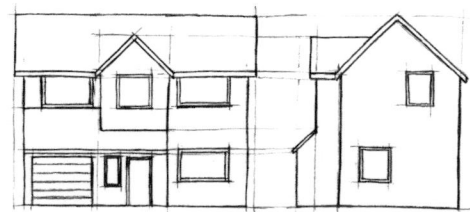

CIRCLES

Sketching circles is made easier by some simple construction.

1. Sketch the box.

- Sketch a square.
- Add diagonals to find the centre of the square.

2. Add centre lines.

- Sketch in two centre lines.
- Mark four points where the centre lines meet the square.

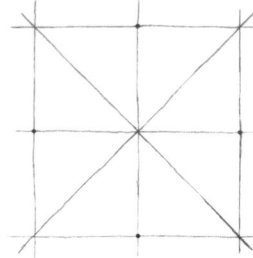

3. Divide the diagonals.

- Divide the diagonals, corner to centre, into four equal parts.

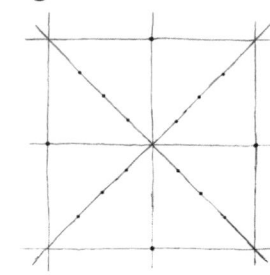

4. Sketch in the circle.

- Sketch in the circle through the outermost eight points.

This method is not exact, but will produce a good circle with practice.

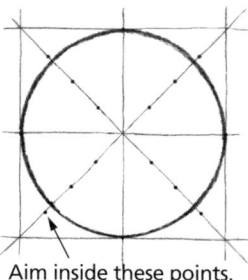

Aim inside these points.

MORE COMPLEX SKETCHES

More complex sketches, such as the clock shown below, can be built up using boxes and circles.

- Concentrate on proportion and line quality.
- Keep construction lines straight and light.
- Plot your circles and curves carefully.
- Firm in outlines and add detail.

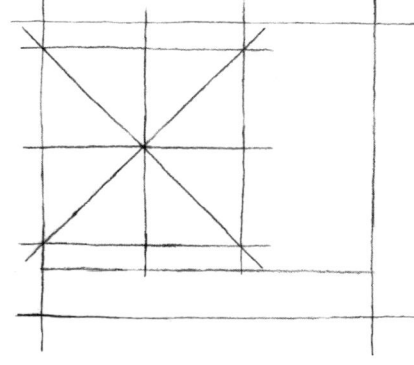

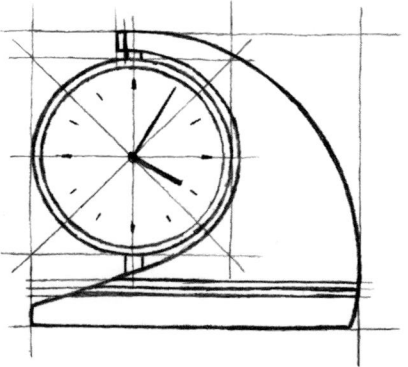

SKETCHING TECHNIQUES – PERSPECTIVE TIPS

INTRODUCTION

Sketching in perspective is an important skill for designers, illustrators and architects. Perspective sketches look realistic and are essential when communicating with customers and clients.

During your course you will sketch, freehand, in perspective. The advice given on page 28 is important. To become skilled in perspective sketching you must:
- turn the paper to sketch lines at your most comfortable sketching angle
- use boxes to build up each sketch
- train your eye to recognise good proportion.

HORIZON LINE AND VANISHING POINTS

VP

- Perspective sketching often starts with a horizon line. It can be placed high or low on the page depending on the effect you want to create.
- The vanishing points (VPs) always lie on the horizon line.

FORESHORTENING (REDUCING THE LENGTHS AND BREADTHS)

- Perspective has the effect of shortening the depths which go back towards the vanishing points.
- This kitchen unit has had its length foreshortened.
- In a row of three identical units, each one is shortened further to create a strong perspective effect.
- Notice that the height also reduces towards the vanishing point.

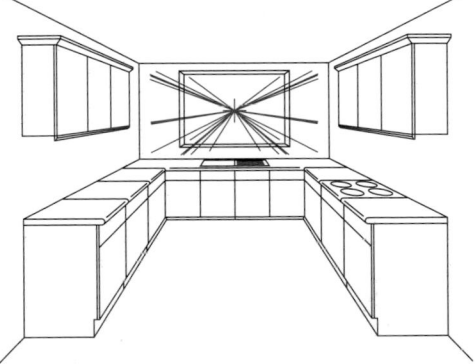

INTERIORS

- One-point perspective (using only one vanishing point) is often used to show interiors such as this kitchen design.
- As in all styles of sketching, creating the correct proportion is the key to success.

SKETCHING PERSPECTIVE CIRCLES AND CYLINDERS

(Use the same construction method as shown for circles on page 28.)

1. Sketch a perspective box.
- Mark a vanishing point.
- Sketch a perspective square. Remember to foreshorten the length.
- Join the diagonals to find the centre.

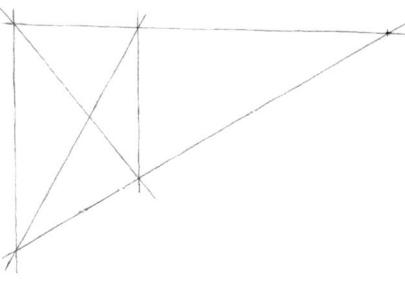

2. Add two centre lines.
- The first line is a vertical centre line.
- The second line projects back to the vanishing point and then extends forward.
- Mark four points where the centre lines meet the perspective square.
- Mark another four points by dividing the diagonals, from the centre to each corner, into four equal parts.

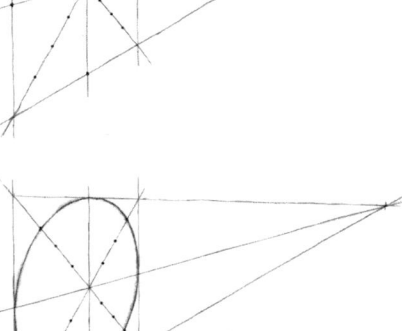

3. Complete the circle.
- Sketch in the circle through each of your eight outermost marks.

4. Sketch a cylinder.
- Add a second vanishing point along the horizon line (note: the horizon line is not shown here for clarity).
- Project the top and bottom of the circle back to the new vanishing point.
- Using the first circle as a guide, sketch in the curve at the back of the cylinder.
- Add detail. This cylinder becomes a torch.

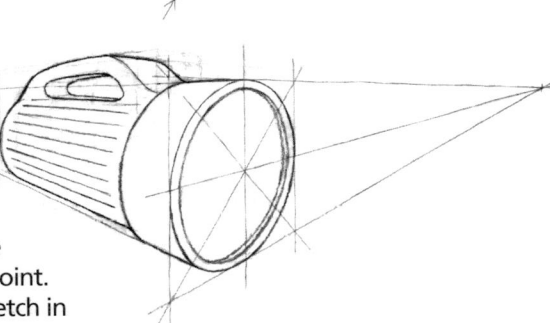

SKETCHING TECHNIQUES – ONE-POINT PERSPECTIVE

INTRODUCTION

Sketching in perspective is the best way to make your sketches look realistic. Illustrators often use perspective to make the products they draw look impressive. Drawing and sketching in perspective can make buildings and products look bigger or more impressive than they really are. One-point perspective sketching uses only one vanishing point.

WORKED EXAMPLE

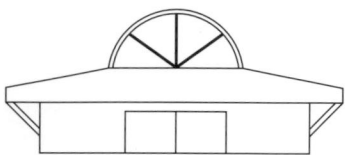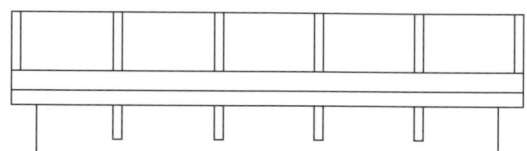

An architect has produced orthographic design drawings for a new leisure pool building. A pictorial sketch is needed to present the design to the client. The architect chooses a one-point perspective sketch. This will be easier for the client to understand and will give a more realistic impression of the building.

1. Sketch the elevation of the pool building.
- Box in the main parts.
- Take care to create the correct proportions.

2. Position the vanishing point carefully.
- Placing it low down will make the building look big and imposing.
- Add sloping roof lines.
- Project the corners back to the vanishing point.
- Check your proportions against the orthographic drawing.

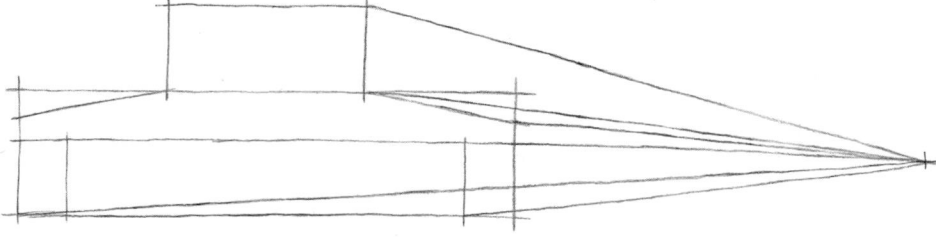

3. Set the front wall back under the roof.
- 'Move' the front wall back towards the vanishing point along the projection lines, taking foreshortening into account.
- Add the back edges of the building and the sloping roof.
- Sketch in the curved glass roof at the front and then at the back.

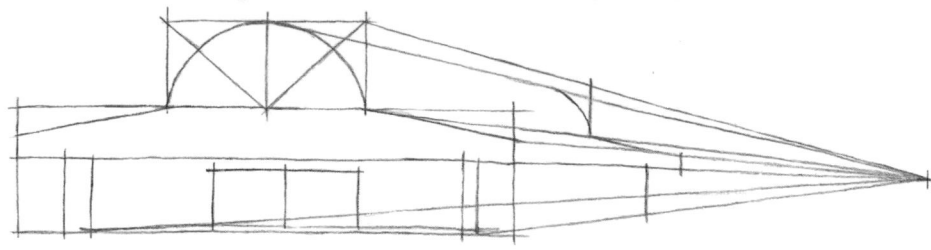

4. Sketch in the curved roof details.
- Curves further back should match those at the front but should be smaller.
- Space out the curved roof frames. The spaces between them become narrower the closer they are to the vanishing point.
- Draw the angled roof supports in the same way.

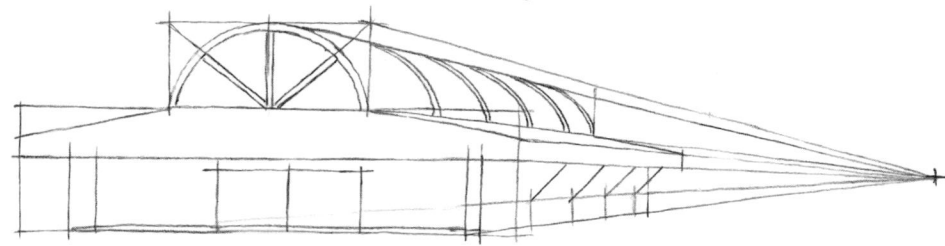

5. Complete the detail and firm in the sketch.
- Make a final check of proportions and foreshortening.
- Add thickness to the roof supports.
- Firm in your sketch.

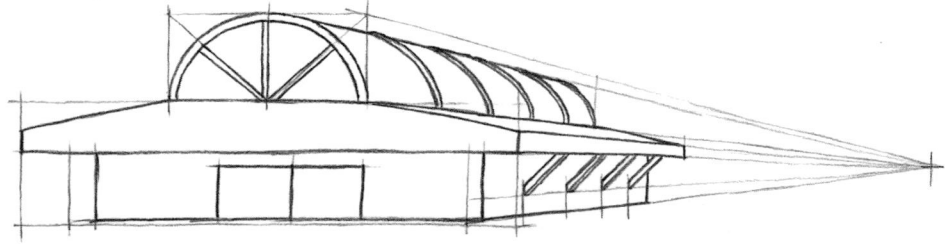

INTRODUCTION

Two-point perspective sketching, as the name suggests, uses two vanishing points. It lets you sketch buildings and objects at any angle.

WORKED EXAMPLE

The elevation and end elevation of a bedside clock are shown. Sketch a two-point perspective view of the clock in good proportion. The position of corner X and two vanishing points (VPs) are given on the answer sheet.

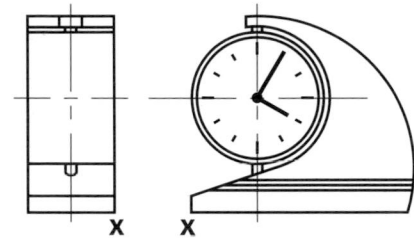

1. Sketch a crate or box.

- Sketch in the front edge of the box and project to the vanishing points.
- Sketch the length and breadth in good proportion.
- Complete the top, working back to the vanishing points.
- Plan the main features inside smaller boxes.
- Use the vanishing points each time.

2. Construct the perspective circle.

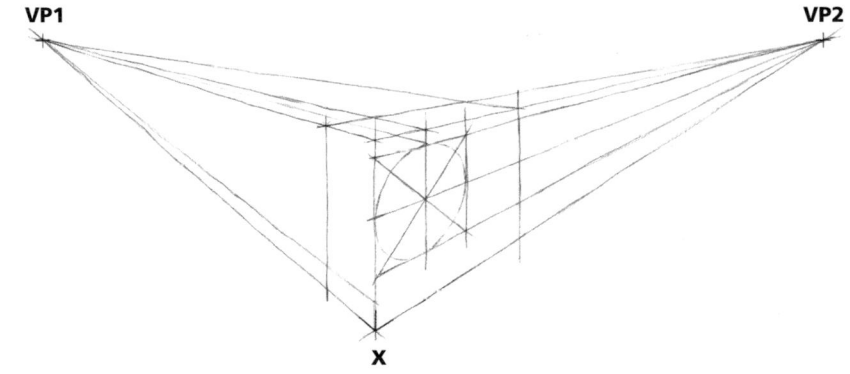

3. Complete one side at a time.

(The right-hand surface is easiest since it has 'flat' surface detail.)

- Sketch in the smaller circle and curve using the first circle as a guide.
- Sketch in the other curves without construction lines.

4. Add depth.

- Project the circle back to vanishing point 1.
- Sketch in the back curve to complete the clock cylinder.
- Do the same with the other curve.

5. Add the details.

- Sketch in the clock face and hands.
- Project the three decorative lines back to vanishing point 2.
- Sketch in the small semicircle at the top.
- Firm in your sketch.

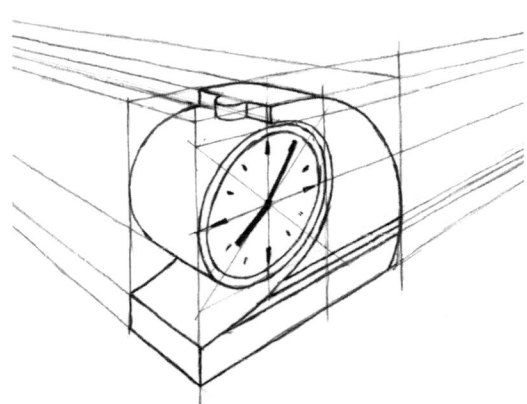

SECTION TWO: KNOWLEDGE AND INTERPRETATION
BUILDING DRAWINGS – LOCATION PLANS AND SITE PLANS

INTRODUCTION

A building or construction project requires a complete set of specialised drawings. These drawings, called a **project set**, are used by the local planning department and building control, as well as by builders, joiners, plumbers, electricians and water, gas and telephone engineers.

The buildings are designed by an architect with a team of technicians and surveyors to help plan and produce the drawings.

The types of drawings you need to know about are:
- location plans
- site (block) plans
- floor plans
- sectional views
- elevations
- schematic diagrams
- illustrations.

You need to understand these drawings and be prepared to answer KI questions about them. You may also be required to add details and symbols to building drawings but, with the exception of elevations, you are not required to complete an entire drawing.

LOCATION PLAN

The location plan is the first drawing in the project set. It identifies the location of the proposed new building within its surroundings. It also helps the builder to plan the layout of a new building scheme and is required by the local government planning department which decides whether or not to approve the project. All building projects come under local authority control.

Neighbouring buildings and their boundaries are shown, as are roads, street names and fields. In the example shown below, the new building is on **plot 6** of a large building project. All the plot numbers are shown.

The new building and plot are outlined with thick black lines and are sometimes, but not always, cross-hatched.

The direction arrow always indicates north.

The **scale** of the drawing depends on the size of the whole building scheme but is normally **1:1250**.

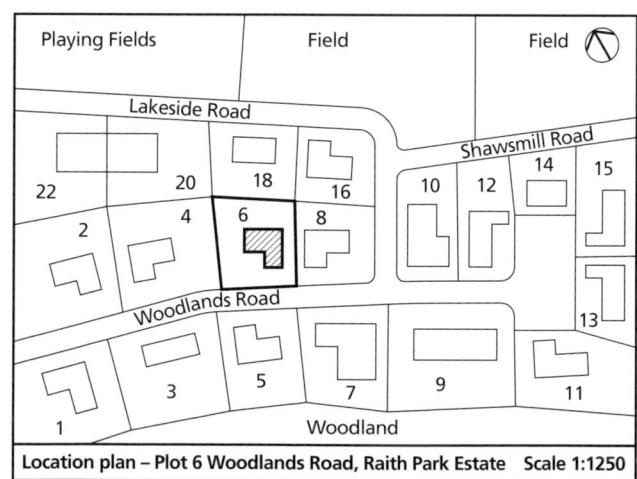

Location plan – Plot 6 Woodlands Road, Raith Park Estate   Scale 1:1250

SITE (BLOCK) PLAN

A site plan (also known as a block plan) shows the site boundary and the outline of the new building which are highlighted in the location plan. Paths, roads and neighbouring plots are also shown. This type of plan enables the builder to mark out the site, lay drainage pipes and build manholes. It is also submitted to the local government planning department for approval.

In this example, two site plans of plot 6 have been drawn – these are shown below.

Site Plan 1

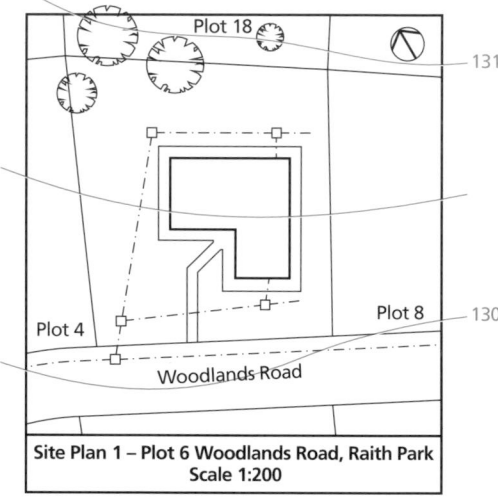

Site Plan 1 – Plot 6 Woodlands Road, Raith Park
Scale 1:200

Site Plan 2

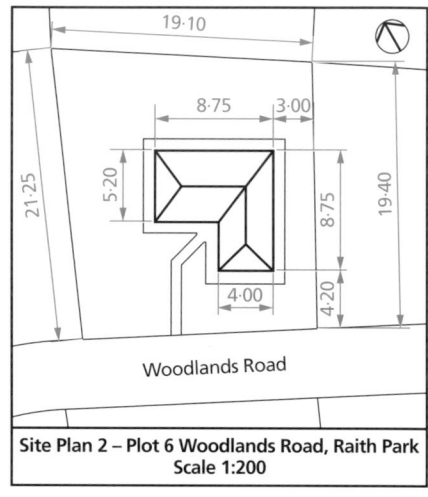

Site Plan 2 – Plot 6 Woodlands Road, Raith Park
Scale 1:200

Site plan 1 shows:
- existing trees
- contour lines which show that the ground slopes down towards the road (the figures are metres above sea level)
- drainage pipes and manholes which run from the bathroom and kitchen to the main drain under the road. The pipes always run downhill.

Site plan 2 shows:
- the building outline, including the roof
- the main dimensions of the house and the site in metres
- the position of the house on the site.

The scale of a site plan depends on the size of the building. For houses and small buildings a **1:200** scale is used.

BUILDING CONTROL AND PLANNING DEPARTMENTS

Drawings for new buildings require approval from the **building control department** and the **planning department** before construction work can begin. The building control department checks that the quality of design and construction meet British standards. The planning department assesses whether or not the style and proportions of the proposed building are appropriate for the location.

BUILDING DRAWINGS – FLOOR PLANS AND SECTIONAL VIEWS

FLOOR PLAN

A floor plan is a type of sectional view. It represents a plan view of the building with the roof and a few layers of bricks removed to show:

• the arrangement of rooms
• the positions of windows and doors
• the types of internal and external walls. In this drawing, external walls are brick cavity walls and internal walls are partition walls made from timber and plasterboard.

Floor plans are used by builders, plumbers, electricians and joiners to help plan the construction work and to cost the building materials.

The scale of a floor plan depends on the size of the building but for most domestic buildings a scale of **1:50** is used. (Note: the drawings on this page are not to scale.)

SIMPLIFIED FLOOR PLAN

Floor plans can be simplified for speed of drawing. In these, the walls are represented by thick lines.

MORE INFO

Other information found on floor plans can include:

• the dimensions of each room and the exact positions of doors and windows
• the layout of water pipes (plumbing)
• the layout of electrical cabling and positions of sockets, switches and fuse boxes.

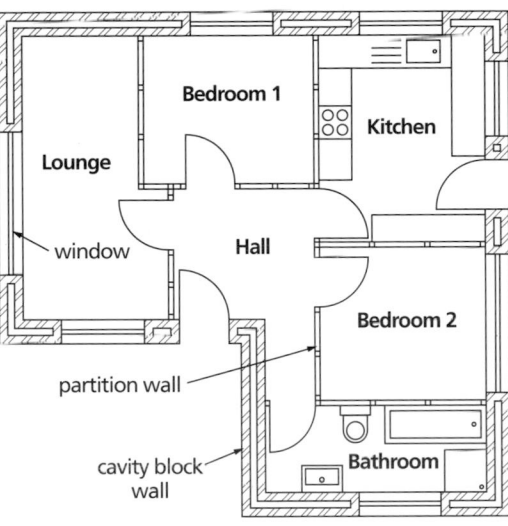

Floor Plan – Plot 6 Woodlands Road, Raith Park
Type: Bungalow   Scale: 1:50

FIXTURES, APPLIANCES AND SYMBOLS

More detailed floor plans show the layout of kitchens and bathrooms, since these are rooms which have fixtures and appliances. BSI symbols (see page 34) are used to simplify the drawing of common features.

The kitchen layout on the right shows electrical and central heating fittings.

HOMEWORK TASK

Using the key to building symbols shown on page 34, identify the common features in the floor plans on this page.

SECTIONAL VIEW

A cross-section showing a slice through the wall gives builders, joiners and roofers a great deal of information about how the house should be built.

The example shown here provides information about:

• the construction of the eaves of the roof
• the type of materials used throughout
• how the window fits into the wall
• the construction of the cavity walls
• the floorboards and joists
• ground levels inside and outside the house
• the design of the foundations.

Sections can be shown through any part of the building and normally a scale of **1:20** is used. The local building control department needs sectional views and floor plans to assess the quality of construction design.

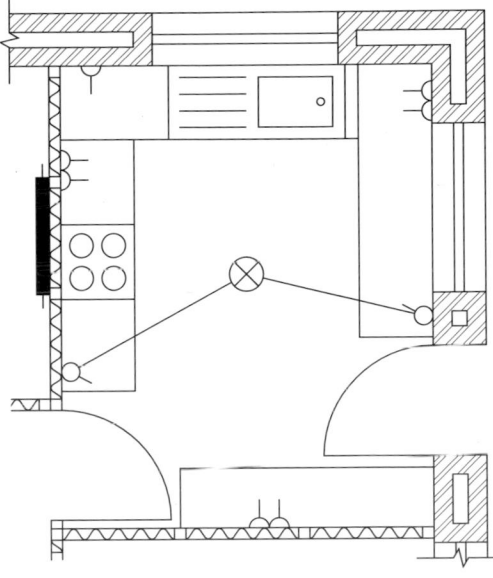

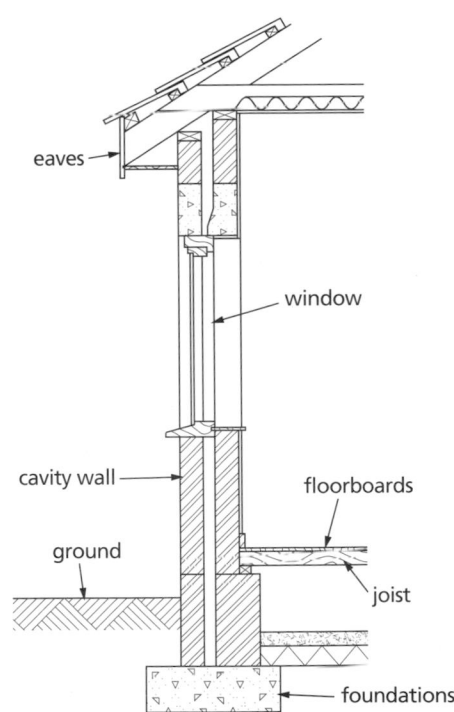

BUILDING DRAWINGS – ELEVATIONS, SCHEMATIC DIAGRAMS AND ILLUSTRATIONS

ELEVATIONS

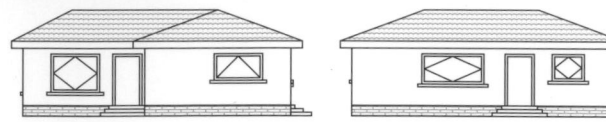

Elevations are orthographic projections of a building produced by its architect or designer. They show:
- the style of the building, e.g. bungalow or villa
- the external appearance of the building
- the style of roof
- the positions of doors, chimneys and windows.

Elevations are required by the local planning department to assess whether the style and proportions of the proposed building are appropriate for the location. Builders also need a picture of what the house will look like from the outside.

BUILDING SYMBOLS

The most common BSI building symbols are shown below. You must understand and remember them.

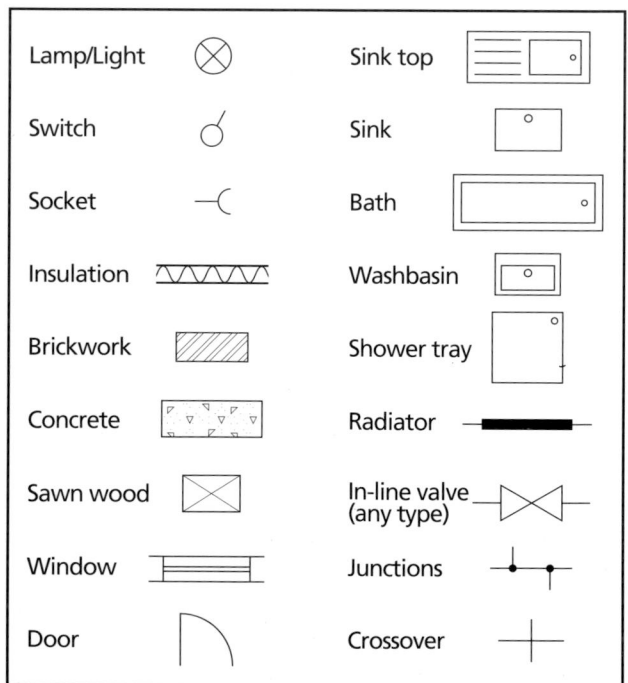

Lamp/Light		Sink top	
Switch		Sink	
Socket		Bath	
Insulation		Washbasin	
Brickwork		Shower tray	
Concrete		Radiator	
Sawn wood		In-line valve (any type)	
Window		Junctions	
Door		Crossover	

SCHEMATIC DIAGRAMS

Heating engineers, plumbers and electricians work from **schematic diagrams**. The purpose of a schematic diagram is to present a complex 3-D installation in a simple 2-D form. Symbols are used to represent common parts such as radiators, valves and water tanks.

Here is an example of a central heating system drawn in 3-D (pictorial) form. The water boiler feeds three radiators. The system is closed, with any water loss topped up from the header tank. Each radiator is controlled by a valve and a pump pushes water around the system.

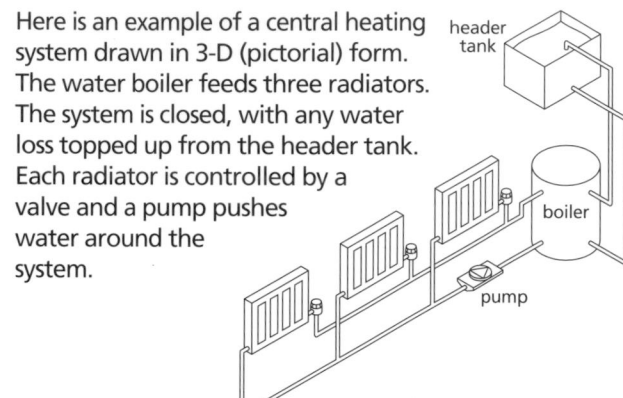

The 3-D layout shown above is complicated and time-consuming to draw. The schematic diagram shown below is much less complicated. BSI symbols are used, and pipes are drawn as thin lines. It is simple and takes much less time to draw.

HOMEWORK TASK

1. From the list of building symbols on the left, identify four symbols which have been used in the schematic diagram above.
2. In this central heating system, what happens to the water at a junction?
3. In the schematic diagram above, what does the arrow beside the pump indicate?

ILLUSTRATIONS AND PROMOTIONAL GRAPHICS

THE GLEN LYON
Our two-bedroom cottage in the exclusive Raith Park estate

Only one in a range of seven styles to be found at our newest development.
Phone or fax for details on **0800 272738/272748**.

Lamont Homes

Selling or renting out the property is an important part of any building project. This often begins before the building work starts. Indeed, it is now common to buy a new house before a brick has been laid.

The process of selling a new building is known as **marketing the property**. It requires a specialised type of graphic known as an illustration.

Illustrations are normally pictorial graphics, although they can be 2-D. They are vital to the marketing plan because:
- they can be drawn in perspective and rendered in colour to make them realistic and attractive to customers
- they promote the property on the market
- they are easily understood by the public because they are not technical graphics
- they can be included in sales brochures for customers
- they can represent the property in pleasant, mature surroundings.

Promotional graphics such as illustrations may be drawn by the architect. However, it is now common to subcontract this work to an illustrator or graphic designer who will produce the illustration and the sales brochure, along with any other promotional materials.

READING AND INTERPRETING COMPLEX DRAWINGS

INTRODUCTION

During your course you will be asked to read and interpret many types of drawings and schematic diagrams. At Credit level these drawings will be more complex than those at General and Foundation levels. Many examples of drawings and symbols can be found in everyday life. Your teacher will provide you with examples from the following list:

- building drawings/site plans/location plans
- plumbing/heating drawings
- assembly/parts drawings of everyday items
- town/railway maps.

You should practise reading and interpreting as wide a range of complex drawings and diagrams as possible to extend your ability in this area.

The examples of a schematic diagram and an exploded view shown here are typical. Other types are displayed throughout this book.

TIPS

- Some drawings may look very complex. Don't worry about this. Take your time and read all the written information.
- Make sure you understand what the question asks you to do.
- Next, study the drawing or schematic and any notes included. A **key** which explains the symbols or labels used may accompany the drawing.
- The drawings will all be in a form you are familiar with, including exploded views, sectional views, assemblies, schematics and building drawings. Study them carefully and piece together your answers, one at a time.

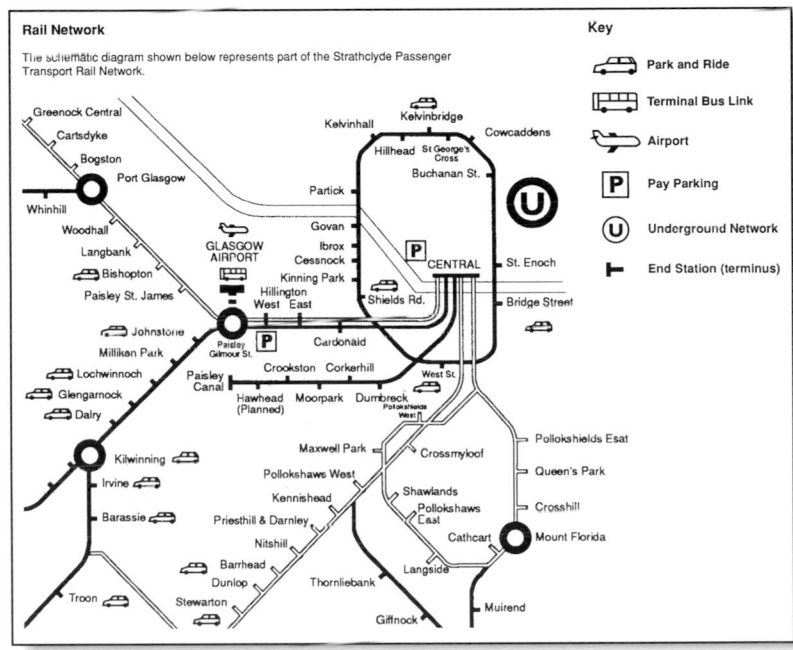

Rail Network

The schematic diagram shown below represents part of the Strathclyde Passenger Transport Rail Network.

Key
- Park and Ride
- Terminal Bus Link
- Airport
- P Pay Parking
- U Underground Network
- End Station (terminus)

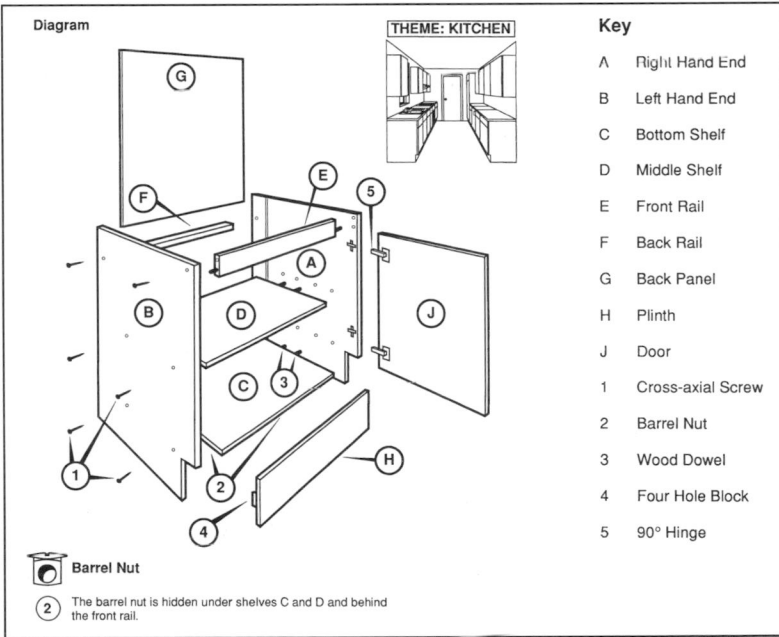

THEME: KITCHEN

Key
- A Right Hand End
- B Left Hand End
- C Bottom Shelf
- D Middle Shelf
- E Front Rail
- F Back Rail
- G Back Panel
- H Plinth
- J Door
- 1 Cross-axial Screw
- 2 Barrel Nut
- 3 Wood Dowel
- 4 Four Hole Block
- 5 90° Hinge

Barrel Nut

2 The barrel nut is hidden under shelves C and D and behind the front rail.

EXAMPLE QUESTIONS

Below are examples of the types of questions you will be asked when reading and interpreting complex diagrams.

Rail Network

The schematic diagram shown on the left represents part of the Strathclyde Passenger Transport Rail Network.

1. Name two stations which are at the end of a line (terminus).

2. How many Park and Ride stations are available from Kilwinning to Troon?

3. Name three stations which are part of the closed loop rail line (the loop which passes through St Enoch).

4. Which stations have Pay Parking available?

5. What does the symbol U stand for?

Kitchen Base Unit

An exploded drawing of a kitchen unit is shown on the left. Study the drawing and refer to the key to answer the following questions.

1. In the drawing, what are the names given to parts B, H and F?

2. Name the two types of fixings used to secure the shelves to the ends of the unit.

3. How many of part 1 are required to construct the kitchen unit?

4. What is used to hold the door in position and how far can each door be opened?

5. How many wooden dowels are used in the assembly of the base unit? (Remember, some may be hidden.)

HOMEWORK TASK

Practise reading and interpreting complex diagrams by answering each of the above questions yourself.

SAFETY SIGNS AND PUBLIC INFORMATION SYMBOLS

INTRODUCTION

Signs and symbols are an important and common form of graphic communication. They are used to communicate safety advice and public information instantly. They break through language barriers because they are graphical. Text is always kept to a minimum.

The signs used in Britain have been standardised by the British Standards Institution. This means that the symbols will be exactly the same wherever they are used in this country.

You must be able to recognise and reproduce (sketch or draw) the symbols shown on this page.

HOMEWORK TASK

Look for each type of sign or symbol in your home, around your town, around your school and in other public buildings. Sketch and colour in examples of two different public information symbols and four different safety signs. Label your sketches to explain which category each one falls into.

PUBLIC INFORMATION SYMBOLS

These are used to inform the public of special needs or conditions.

Kitemark
Shows that the BSI have checked the manufacturer's claims that the product complies in every way with the standards quoted. It also shows that the manufacturer's production system is being monitored. This symbol is very prestigious. Look for it on household products.

Safety Mark
Shows that the product has been checked to British Standards specifications for safety.

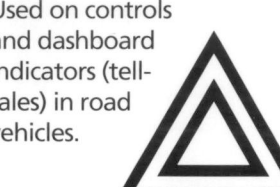

Hazard Warning
Used on controls and dashboard indicators (tell-tales) in road vehicles.

Fragile
Used on packaging

Keep Dry
Used on packaging

This way up
Used on packaging

Male/Female
Used at changing rooms and toilets, etc.

BRITISH AND EUROPEAN SAFETY SIGNS

These signs inform, instruct or warn the public. Their message is contained in the shape and colour of the sign and the symbol displayed. Study and remember the standardised shapes and colours used in each type. The design of each sign remains constant but different symbols can be used inside each sign.

Mandatory signs
Blue circular background with white symbol, e.g. eye protection must be worn.

Warning signs
Yellow triangular background with black band, e.g. risk of electric shock.

Firefighting signs
Red square background with white symbol or text, e.g. fire alarm.

Prohibition signs
White circular background with red band and cross bar, e.g. no smoking.

Safe condition signs
Green square/rectangular background with white symbol or text, e.g. first aid, indication of direction.

Danger identification
Used to identify the perimeter of a hazard. The stripes are black and luminous yellow or orange.

FLOW CHARTS

INTRODUCTION

Flow charts are a convenient way of showing the order in which tasks must be carried out. They are often used in business – for example, to describe office procedures – and in the development of computer programs.

Different shapes are used to show different types of actions. Arrows are used to show the direction in which the tasks are worked through. The shapes of the boxes follow British Standards.

FLOW CHART SYMBOLS

Here are the flow chart symbols you need to know:

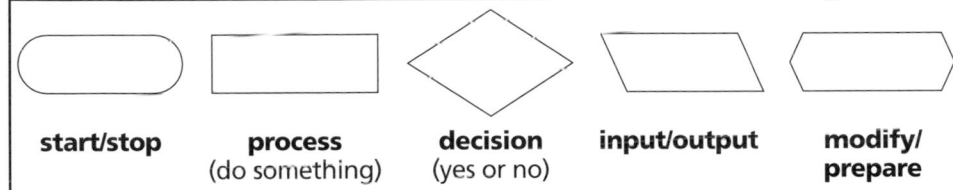

start/stop **process** (do something) **decision** (yes or no) **input/output** **modify/ prepare**

A TYPICAL FLOW CHART LAYOUT

- First you **start**.

- Next you carry out a **process (task)**.

- **Decide** whether this task is successful.

- Carry out the next task.

- Decide whether this task is successful.

- Then **stop**.

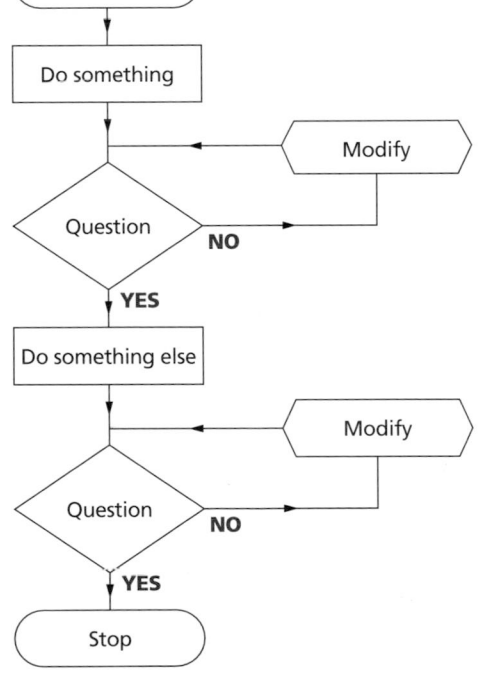

EXAMPLE 1

A flow chart for saving a computer drawing onto a floppy disc

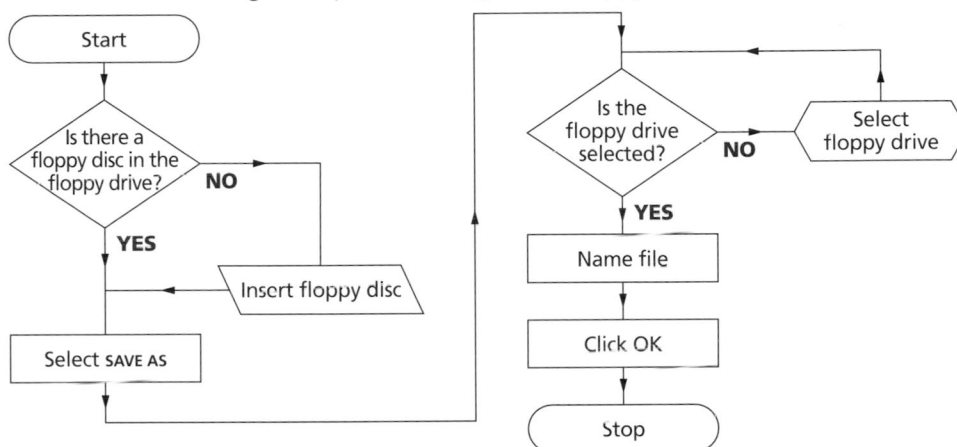

EXAMPLE 2

A more complicated flow chart showing the stages and decisions in one turn in a game of Snakes and Ladders

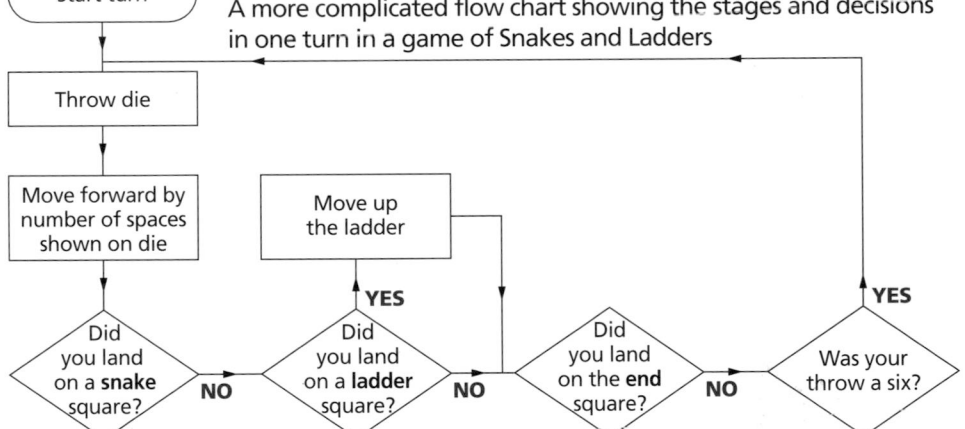

HOMEWORK TASK

Make up a flow chart for switching on a television set and selecting the correct channel to watch a TV show.

CIRCUIT DIAGRAMS

INTRODUCTION

During your course you will learn to recognise and draw electrical symbols and construct circuit diagrams. A pictorial schematic drawing of an electrical system is usually provided and you will be asked to draw a circuit diagram.

British Standards symbols are shown below. Using these symbols saves drawing time and ensures consistent standards across the country.

Standardised symbols are used in such industries as building, engineering, plumbing and electrical work. It is important that you become familiar with these conventions and the work of the British Standards Institution (see page 6).

CIRCUIT DIAGRAM SYMBOLS

Here are the electrical symbols you need to know:

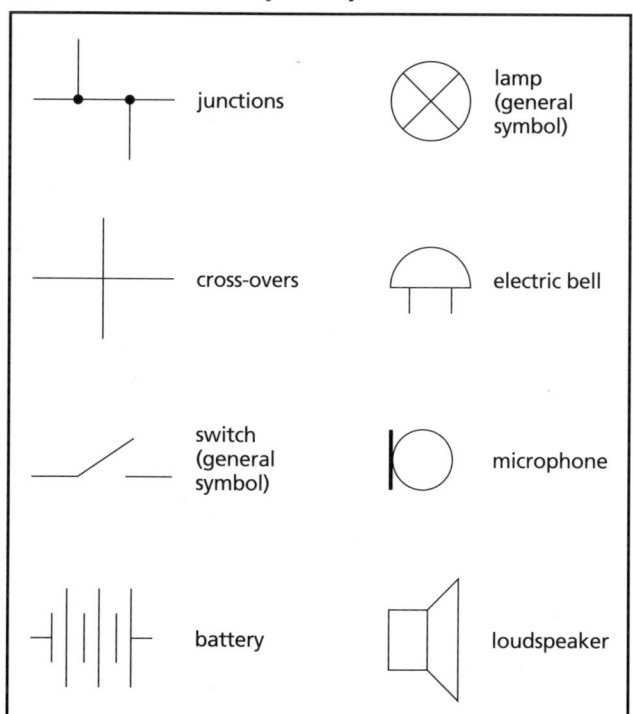

junctions	lamp (general symbol)
cross-overs	electric bell
switch (general symbol)	microphone
battery	loudspeaker

WORKED EXAMPLE

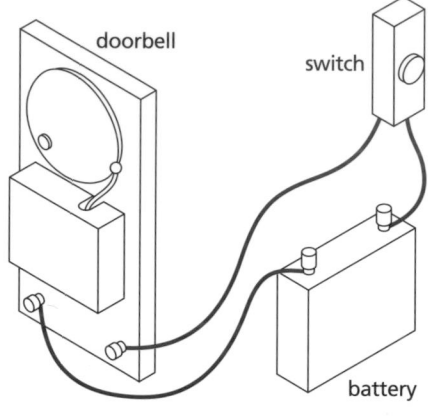

pictorial drawing

A pictorial drawing of a doorbell circuit is shown. It contains three main components: a bell, a battery and a push switch. Complete the circuit diagram by adding the correct symbols.

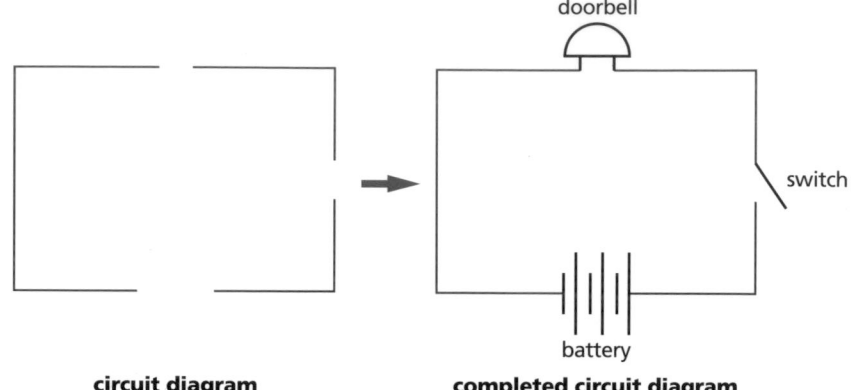

circuit diagram
(showing wires only)

completed circuit diagram
(showing symbols to represent electrical components)

HOMEWORK TASK

From the pictorial drawing of a street entertainer's sound system, complete the circuit diagram shown.

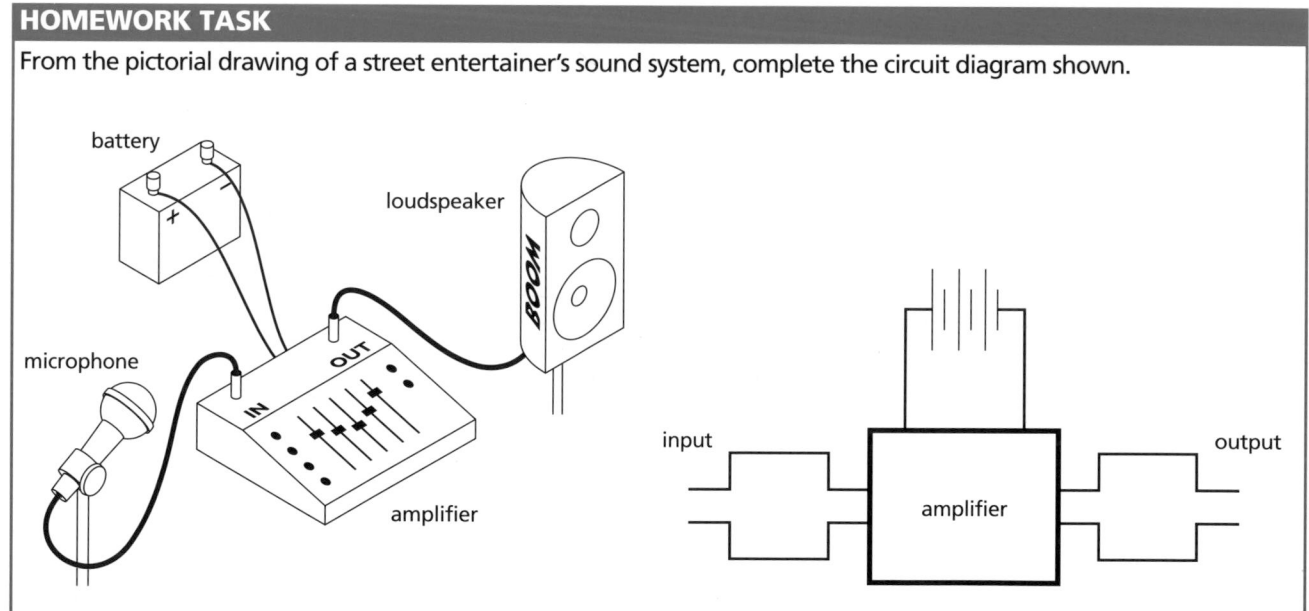

SEQUENCE DIAGRAMS AND STORYBOARDS

INTRODUCTION

Sequence diagrams are used to show graphically how to perform a task correctly and efficiently. Lengthy explanations can be difficult to follow and lead to confusion. A good sequence diagram shows the information clearly and in a logical order.

Sequence diagrams are often used to plan projects such as films, stage productions or advertising campaigns and are known as **storyboards**.

Examples of sequence diagrams can be found in the user guides for most household products. For example, your video recorder or bicycle will almost certainly have come with instructions for assembly and/or use. Reading and interpreting existing sequence diagrams is excellent practice for this KI topic.

Your teacher may ask you to produce a storyboard to plan the production of a portfolio graphic and you may need to interpret or sketch a sequence diagram in your course exam.

Here are some examples of everyday situations where sequence diagrams may be found:

- buying a hot drink or a sweet from a vending machine
- using a public telephone
- assembling a Lego model
- assembling a computer system
- assembling flatpack furniture
- loading a camera with a new film.

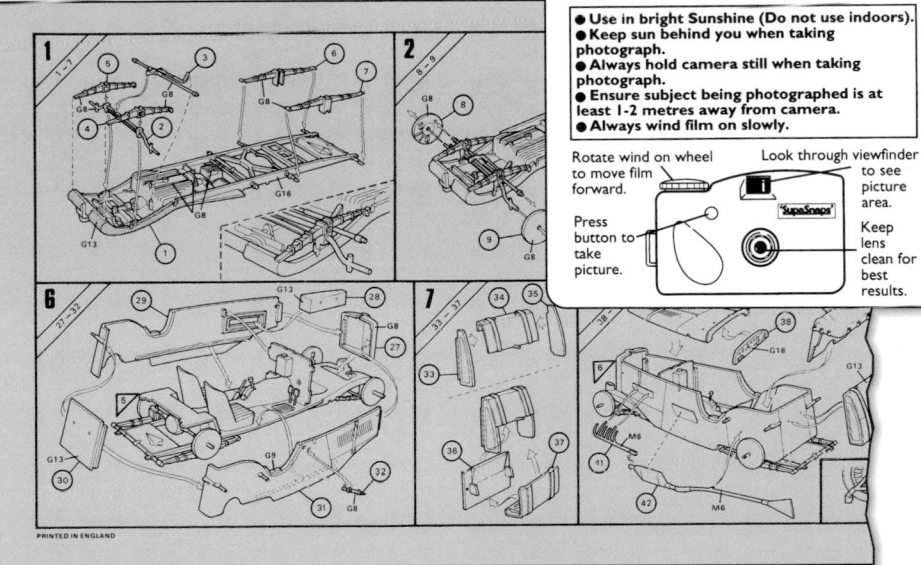

PRODUCING A SEQUENCE DIAGRAM OR STORYBOARD

When producing a sequence diagram or storyboard:

- first plan out the stages of the sequence diagram by writing a list
- design graphics to illustrate the main stages
- keep the graphics simple and clear
- keep the text to a minimum.

EXAMPLE: USING A LOCKER

HOMEWORK TASK

Select an everyday product and produce a sequence diagram to explain how it is used.

COLOUR – BASICS

INTRODUCTION

The use of colour plays an important part in illustration and graphic design. Colour is used to make graphics look realistic and to help designers create a mood or feeling.

Questions on colour can appear in the *Knowledge and Interpretation* part of the exam. In your *Illustration and Presentation* portfolio you will be expected to select and use colour, and to give reasons for your choices.

PRIMARY COLOURS

The **primary colours** – **red**, **yellow** and **blue** – are the three colours which are mixed together to produce all the other colours.

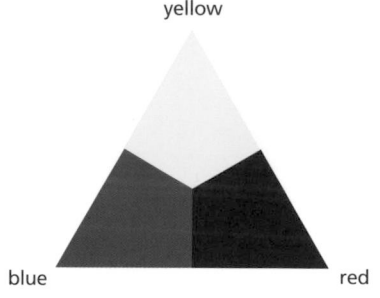

TERTIARY COLOURS

Tertiary colours are made when a primary colour and a secondary colour are mixed in equal quantity. They take their name from the two mixed colours, e.g. red and orange make red-orange.

THE COLOUR WHEEL

The **colour wheel** (shown on the right) was designed as a way of showing how colours relate to each other. The outside ring shows the **three primary**, **three secondary** and **six tertiary** colours.

SECONDARY COLOURS

The **secondary colours** – **violet**, **orange** and **green** – are made by mixing two primary colours in equal quantities (e.g. red and yellow make orange).

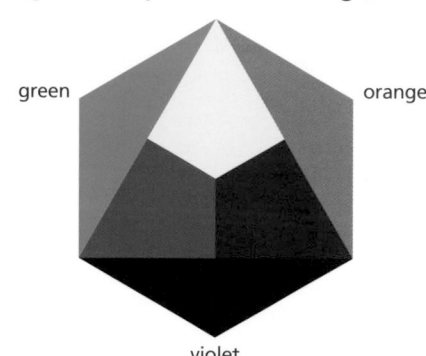

HARMONY

Harmony is created when colours close to each other on the outside of the colour wheel are used together. Harmony is easy on the eye. For example, the blue and green in this bottle create a relaxing image.

CONTRAST

Contrast occurs when colours far apart on the colour wheel are used together. Contrast is eye-catching and makes objects stand out. Contrasting colours are described as **complementary**. For example, in this bottle the green makes the red look redder and the red makes the green look greener.

WARM COLOURS

Reds, **yellows** and **oranges** are **warm colours**, i.e. they give feelings of warmth. They are also known as **advancing colours** because they appear to be closer to the viewer than other colours. For example, if you painted your bedroom in these colours it would seem warm but it would also feel smaller because warm colours make the walls look closer.

COOL COLOURS

Blues, **greens** and **violets** do exactly the opposite. They give feelings of being cold and are known as **cool colours**. They also appear to be further away and are called **receding colours**. For example, if you painted your bedroom in these colours it would appear cold but it would also feel bigger because cool colours make the walls look more distant.

COLOUR – TONE AND COLOUR SCHEMES

TONE

Tone is the term used to describe how strong or weak a colour is. All colours can be produced in a full range of tones from strong tones with lots of depth to weak tones which are very pale. You will learn how to apply different tones on page 56.

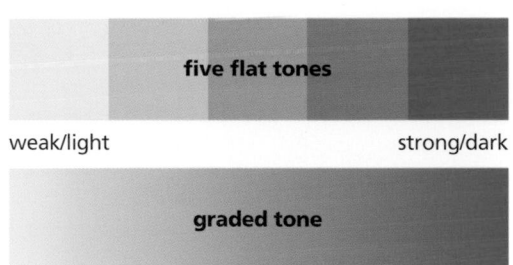

five flat tones

weak/light   strong/dark

graded tone

THE EFFECTS OF LIGHT ON SURFACES

Surface tones on 3-D objects change depending on the way light falls on the surface.

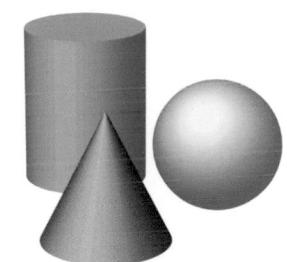

On **flat-sided** objects such as cuboids, the tone on the surface facing the light source is pale, while the tone on the surface facing away from the light source is dark or strong. Each surface has a **flat tone**.

Objects with **curved surfaces** reflect light differently. The tone on a curved surface changes from dark to light as the surface curves toward the light source. This is called **graded tone**. Cylinders, spheres and cones have graded surface tones.

TINTS AND SHADES

Tints and **shades** help designers by increasing the colour options they can use. Designers rarely work with pure colours. Instead, they use tints and shades to create different moods and feelings.

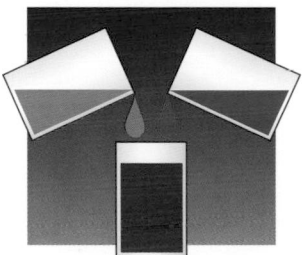

Add **white** to make a **tint**. Pale pastel colours give the impression of softness.

Add **black** or **grey** to make a **shade**. Dark shades make objects appear heavy.

CHOOSING A COLOUR SCHEME

Interior designers and graphic designers are very careful when they choose colour schemes. As a simple rule, designers use only two or three main colours. To help them, they use colour charts and colour wheels similar to one shown on page 40 but with many more colours, including tints and shades. An example of a designer's colour wheel is shown on the right.

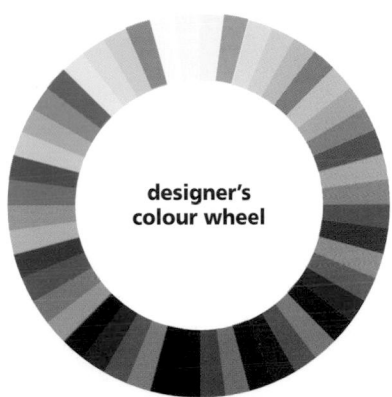

designer's colour wheel

TIPS FOR CHOOSING A COLOUR SCHEME

When choosing a colour scheme, use **one** of the following rules. It will help you to put together an effective and balanced colour scheme.

1. Any colours **near each other** (within any **third** of the colour wheel) will always work together to create a **harmonious colour scheme**.

or

2. Any two colours which are **opposite each other** on the colour wheel look good together and make a **bold scheme**.

or

3. Any three colours which are **equally spaced** on the colour wheel work together to make an **exciting scheme**.

HOMEWORK TASK

Look carefully at the colours used in the two graphics below. Pick out the colours used from the designer's colour wheel. Which of the three colour schemes from the above tips list do they each satisfy?

texttexttexttext

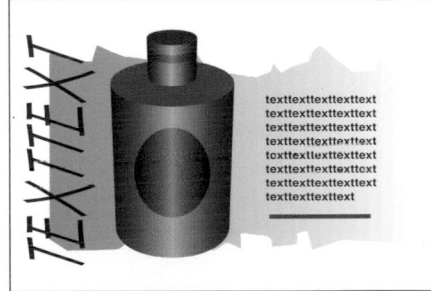

COLOUR – COLOUR IN COMMUNICATION

COLOUR AND MOODS

Different colours create different moods and feelings. Designers make use of this by selecting colours which help to support the atmosphere they want to create. This page gives examples of the moods that different colours create. This knowledge will help you when you are choosing colours for your own layouts and graphics. When you design, don't select colours individually; instead, think of the effects created by colour combinations.

THE FUNCTION OF COLOUR IN COMMUNICATION

Colour is widely used in communication:
- as a symbol, e.g. in flags
- to give instructions, e.g. in traffic lights
- to show group identity, e.g. in team colours
- to organise and identify, e.g. in colour-coding
- to promote businesses, e.g. in company logos and corporate colours
- to promote sales, e.g. in packaging.

HOMEWORK TASK

Select a large colour advertisement from a magazine. Write a brief report about the advertisement which:
- identifies the target market (who the poster is aimed at)
- states why the colours have been chosen (what mood has been created)
- identifies where contrast and harmony have been used.

RED

warm, exciting, vibrant, passionate, dangerous, revolutionary, active, aggressive, courageous, festive

GREEN

cool, restful, natural, calm, soothing, fresh, quiet, informal

VIOLET

cool, peaceful, solitary

ORANGE

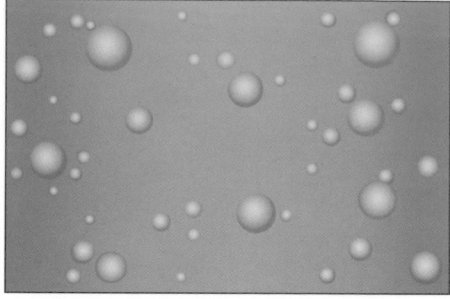

warm, happy, sunny, cheerful, appetising – full of flavour and energy

BLUE

cool, elegant, sophisticated, heavenly, formal, classy

NEUTRALS

greys: natural, restful, calm, elegant, dignified, comfortable
browns: natural, earthy, safe, reliable, good

YELLOW

warm, happy, sunny, lively, cheerful, glowing, sparkling, bright – most easily seen

PURPLE

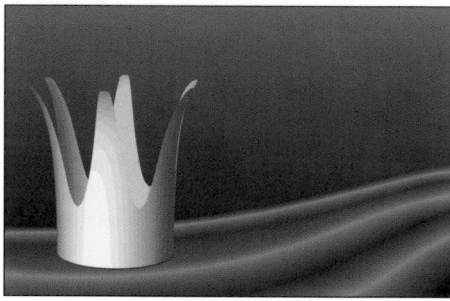

rich, pompous, regal

BLACK AND WHITE

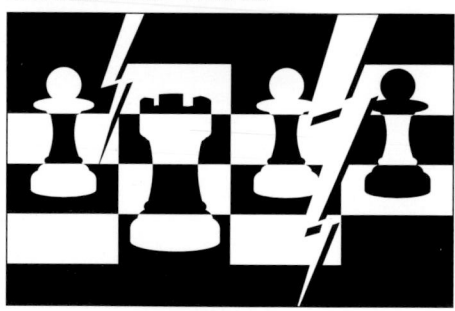

dramatic, elegant, stylish, sophisticated, pure, opposing, contrasting

COMPUTER-AIDED GRAPHICS (CAG) – ADVANCED APPLICATIONS AND HARDWARE

INTRODUCTION

The development of computers has significantly changed the ways in which graphics are produced. Recent advances in computer technology enable designers to create complex and realistic graphic images quickly and easily. Two examples of advanced computer graphics are animation and simulation.

COMPUTER ANIMATION

Animation (moving images) was traditionally created by drawing thousands of 'still' graphics by hand. Each one progressed the movement a little bit further. It was a very slow and labour intensive process. Modern **animation software** creates on-screen movement by moving graphic images along plotted paths. It is **quick, smooth and realistic.** Computer animation is used to increase the **visual impact** of graphics on the viewer. A product with **moving parts** can be animated to demonstrate how it works, e.g. an elevator in a design for a new office building. Animation can also assist in **education** and **training**, e.g. to show how blood flows around the body.

COMPUTER SIMULATION

Computer simulation uses computer models to imitate or predict behaviour in real life situations. A realistic experience is provided within a simulated environment. **Training, testing** and **predicting outcomes** are the areas in which simulation is most useful.

- 3-D simulators are commonly used to **train** pilots or drivers how to cope in dangerous situations such as landing an aeroplane or driving a tank in battle. The user can '**interact**' with the simulation and control his/her vehicle with a joystick.
- In civil engineering, simulation can **test** the design of a structure that would be too big to make a prototype of, e.g. **testing** the stability of ships or the strength of a bridge.
- In car design, the body shape is **tested** for wind resistance even before a prototype is built.
- In medicine, surgeons often make use of simulated operations to **predict** the difficulties of a medical procedure before the patient is put at risk.
- In weather forecasting, simulations of weather systems are used to **predict** the weather.
- Computer models can be modified in '**real time**' to improve performance.

HARDWARE AND SOFTWARE

Computer systems use a combination of **hardware** and **software** to perform tasks. Hardware is the name given to the physical parts of a system – both internal (such as CPU, RAM and hard drive) and external (such as keyboard, monitor and printer). Software is the name given to the programs which interact with the hardware, enabling the computer to perform its tasks.

Hardware and software work together to move information between the areas of the computer which deal with **input**, **processing**, **storage** and **output**.

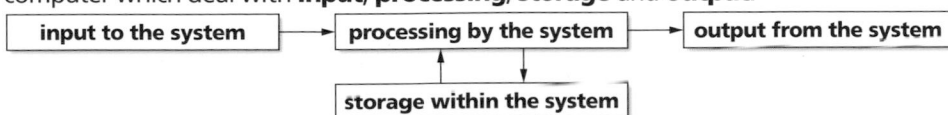

Processing is carried out by the CPU using information stored in memory. Disc drives provide storage. Devices such as keyboards and monitors provide input and output.

INSIDE A TYPICAL PERSONAL COMPUTER (PC)

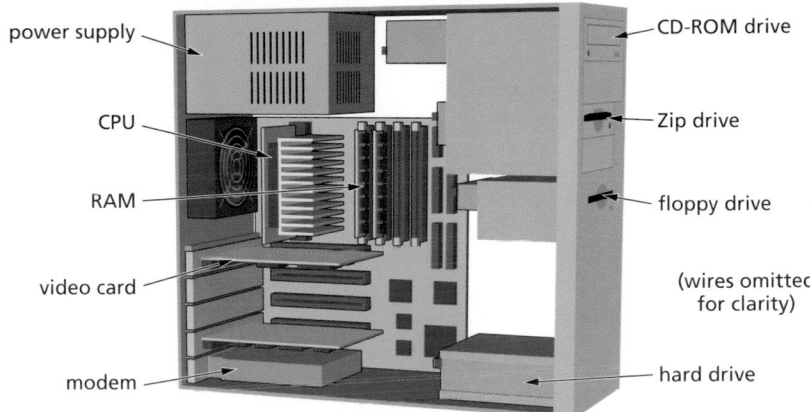

- **CPU (Central Processing Unit)** – the computer's 'brain'; a large microchip where program instructions are carried out and data is processed. Modern CPUs are very fast and can process vast numbers of instructions (e.g. 10^{10} multiplications per second). Graphics programs require fast CPUs and video cards.
- **RAM (Random Access Memory)** – temporary storage based on microchips; holds programs and data while they are being used. Very fast, but can only hold information while the computer is on. To run efficiently, graphics programs require lots of RAM. 384 MB is typical. A computer system becomes more powerful as the amount of RAM and the speed and power of the CPU and video card increase.
- **ROM (Read-only Memory)** – permanent storage which cannot be altered by the user. Modern PCs contain a small ROM microchip which holds a simple start-up program used when the computer is switched on.
- **hard drive** – high storage-capacity, typically 30GB, semi-permanent storage based on magnetic discs in a sealed box; used to hold programs and data while they are not in use. Information remains on disc even while the computer is switched off. Some modern hard drives are removable and can be locked away in a safe when not in use.
- **CD-ROM drive** – medium storage-capacity removable-disc drive; data on CD-ROM disc is 'read-only', i.e. it can be read but cannot be altered. (Some computers now have CD-R [recordable CD] or high-capacity DVD drives instead.) Computer software and clipart are often supplied on CD-ROM.
- **floppy drive** – low storage-capacity removable-disc drive; data can be written to and read from floppy discs. A **Zip drive** is similar to a floppy drive, but has a higher capacity.
- **video (graphics) card** – converts computer data to a video signal suitable for display on a monitor. Modern video cards can display complex 2-D and 3-D images very quickly.
- **modem** – both an input and an output device; connects a computer to a telephone network, allowing communication between computers on different sites.
- **Memory** and disc capacities are measured in **bytes**. (A byte is a single unit of data.) 1KB (kilobyte) = 1024 bytes   1MB (megabyte) = 1024KB   1GB (gigabyte) = 1024MB

COMPUTER SYSTEMS

Computer systems can be categorised as small-scale, medium-scale and large-scale systems, according to the amount of processing work they can handle.

Small scale – Personal Computers (PC)

PCs (also known as 'microcomputers') are either 'desktop' or 'portable' units.

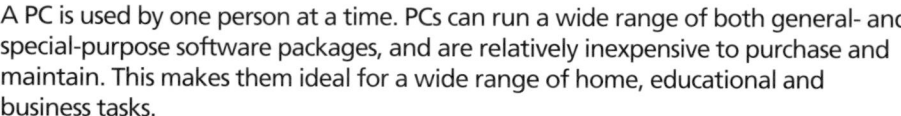

- A **desktop PC** is fairly large and designed to sit on a desk. The main unit, monitor, keyboard and other parts are usually separate units which are connected by cables, and the whole system is mains-powered.

- A **portable PC**, often known as a **laptop**, is a small, battery-powered computer which can be as powerful as a desktop PC. Miniature components and a flat-screen LCD (Liquid Crystal Display) reduce this PC to the size of a small briefcase.

A PC is used by one person at a time. PCs can run a wide range of both general- and special-purpose software packages, and are relatively inexpensive to purchase and maintain. This makes them ideal for a wide range of home, educational and business tasks.

Medium scale – Workstations

A workstation is a very fast microcomputer which provides more processing power than a desktop PC. Workstations are used in industry and universities to perform specialised tasks, for example, high-end 3-D graphics work and data processing. Like a PC, a workstation is used by one person at a time.

Large scale – Mainframes

A mainframe is an extremely powerful computer designed to process vast quantities of data. Mainframes are very large – the main processing unit alone often fills an entire room. Many users can use a single mainframe at the same time, accessing it through simple 'terminals' (essentially just a keyboard and monitor connected to the mainframe via a network). Mainframes are very expensive to purchase and maintain, and the software they run is highly specialised. They are mainly used by businesses such as banks, which require huge amounts of fast, centralised data processing.

COMPUTER NETWORKS

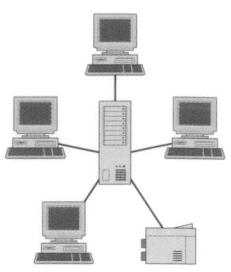

Computer networks connect computers together and enable computer users on different machines, often in different locations, to communicate directly with one another and share data quickly and conveniently.

Networks can connect computers across small distances (within the same room or building) to allow users to share peripheral devices such as printers and scanners, as well as exchange data.

Networks can also cover very large distances (between different towns or countries). Computers on large networks may use **modems** to connect to one another via the telephone system. The **Internet**, for example, is a massive computer network which spans the globe and has a huge number of users.

Many network systems use specialised computers called **servers** to store files in a single, central location. Servers contain fast, high-capacity hard drives, allowing them to store large amounts of data. Individual computers connect to a common server, allowing users to store files at and retrieve files from a single location.

THE INTERNET

The Internet is used by many different types of people and organisations, including individuals, businesses, schools, colleges and universities. Many types of services are available on the Internet. The most commonly used services are:

- **e-mail** – an electronic 'postal service' which allows users to send typed messages (and sometimes files) to each other by using e-mail programs
- **FTP** (File Transfer Protocol) – a system which allows users to share files across the internet. Users can 'upload' (send) files to a internet server where they are made available for other users to 'download' (retrieve)
- **newsgroups** – discussion sites where users can discuss topics of interest. Users can read and post messages in newsgroups of their choice
- the **World Wide Web** – a system for giving users access to millions of pages of information which are stored on internet servers. Each web page has a unique address called a URL (Uniform Resource Locator), e.g. http://www.leckieandleckie.co.uk. A collection of web pages is known as a website. Many organisations, including businesses, schools and individual users, have their own websites, allowing them to communicate information and advertise to Internet users around the world.

Many businesses use the Internet to communicate with customers worldwide. For example, architects and design engineers can communicate with subcontractors and component suppliers, allowing changes to a design to be viewed instantly by all parties. Designers can exchange ideas and drawings with colleagues around the world. Clients can explore virtual reality 'walk throughs' of 3-D model designs from anywhere in the world.

CAG – FILE STORAGE AND MANAGEMENT

FILE MANAGEMENT

File management is the process of organising and storing data on computer. When you save a piece of work you've created in a software application, that work is stored as a **file**, either on the computer's hard disc or on a recordable, removable disc. It is very important that you look after the files you produce during your CAG work. If your files are lost before the work is finished and a printout (hard copy) is made for your portfolio, you will have to do that work all over again!

Different types of computer deal with file management in slightly different ways, but the basic principles are the same. Work is stored in the form of files. The user can organise these files by saving or moving them into suitable **folders** (also known as **directories**). New folders can be created as required. Old files and folders can be deleted when they are no longer needed.

TIP

Imagine that a computer disc is like a drawer of a filing cabinet. Paper documents (files) can be organised into cardboard folders (folders) within that drawer (disc). This keeps them tidy and ensures that they will be easy to find again later.

It is very easy to lose work if you don't organise your files sensibly and neatly. For example, in the diagram shown here the file 'Graphs and Charts text' has been saved into the folder 'Graphs and Charts'. This folder lies within the folder 'Sarah Black's CAG Work'. This is an example of good organisation.

Your school may have its own rules and advice on where and how students should save and organise their work, so ask your teacher before you begin.

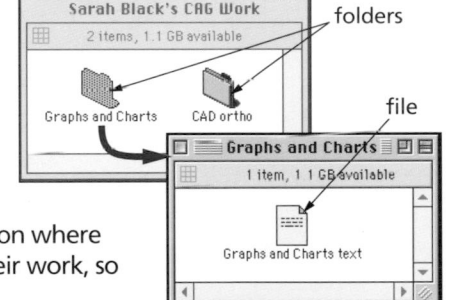

TIPS

- When saving work for the first time, always give it a full, descriptive name so that you can easily identify the file later (e.g. 'Graphs and Charts text', not 'text').
- Always put files in an appropriately labelled folder. For example, if you are using a shared computer in a classroom and saving your files on its hard disc, first create a new folder and give it a suitable name, e.g. 'Sarah Black's CAG Work'. Next create additional folders within this one: one for Graphs and Charts work, one for CAD Ortho work, and so on. As you work, save each file to the appropriate folder.
- Always keep **back-ups** of your files. Back-up copies should be made on a different disc to the original file. For example, if the original file is saved on hard disc, then the back-up is made by copying the file to a floppy disc. If the original file is kept on a removable disc, then make the back-up onto a second removable disc. This way, if the original file is later lost or damaged, it can be replaced from the back-up disc.

REMOVABLE DISCS

A PC usually contains several disc drives: an internal hard drive and one or more removable-disc drives. Whilst the hard drive is normally used for most general, day-to-day storage of work, recordable, removable discs have three important uses:

- **copying/moving files** – When computers are not connected by a network, the easiest way to transfer files between one machine and another is by copying the files onto a removable disc which is then taken to the destination PC.

- **backing-up files** – Back-up copies of important files are taken as insurance against files being accidentally (or deliberately) deleted or corrupted.

- **archiving files** – When files are no longer being worked on and are not needed regularly, they are usually copied onto a durable removable disc (often CD-R) and then deleted from the computer's hard drive. This frees up valuable storage space on the hard drive, preventing it from running out of room.

There are several types of recordable, removable discs in common use:

- **3.5" floppy disc** – a magnetic medium which allows computer data to be recorded. Storage capacity: 1·44 MB

- **Zip disc** – a magnetic medium similar to the floppy disc. Storage capacity: 100 MB or 250 MB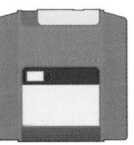

- **Recordable Compact Disc (CD-R)** – an optical medium which can be read in any CD-ROM drive, though requires a special drive to record. Storage capacity: 650 MB

- **Digital Versatile Disc (DVD)** – an optical medium similar to CD-ROM. Recordable DVD-R ('record once') and rewritable DVD-RAM ('record many times') formats are available. Storage capacity: 4·7 GB, 9·4 GB or 17 GB.

MORE INFO

You must always handle removable discs with great care. If a disc is lost or damaged then the work it contains may be lost too.
- Always label discs, clearly indicating their contents. Also include your name and class.
- Always store discs in protective disc boxes when not in use.
- Never force a disc into a disc drive.
- Never eject a disc while the disc light is on.
- Never place heavy objects on top of discs.
- Always keep discs away from dust, water, strong sunlight and high temperatures.
- Always keep magnetic discs away from magnetic sources (e.g. monitors and speakers).
- Never leave discs lying around unattended.

INPUT DEVICES
(QWERTY) Keyboard

The keyboard includes letter, number and function keys. These keys are used to produce letters or numbers on the screen or to send commands to the computer. Each key is a switch which sends a particular code to the computer.

Mouse

The mouse is used to guide a pointer (cursor) around on the screen. Functions are selected by clicking control buttons. Mice detect movement optically (using a reflected beam of light) or by sensing a ball turning against rollers as the mouse moves. The mouse is the **most common input device** for **graphics work**.

Trackerball

This device is very similar to a computer mouse in its operation. However, the larger ball is positioned on top with the operator's fingers directing the cursor's actions around the screen. It **needs very little desk space** and no mouse mat.

Joystick

Computer joysticks often look very similar to aircraft joysticks. They are very popular with computer gamers as they give a **realistic feel** for the on-screen action. They are used to control movement in **flight simulations** and to manoeuvre tanks through **battlefield simulations**.

Graphics tablet

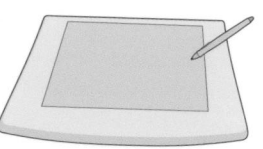

This is **quick to use** and gives **pinpoint accuracy**. An electronic table or tablet constantly detects the position of a puck or stylus. A graphics tablet senses **position** (unlike a mouse which can only sense movement), so it is ideal for **tracing line drawings** from paper and for 'sketching' in a painting program. They are also used in industry to **insert CAD library parts** on-screen.

Digital stills camera

This device saves images in a digital form. These images can be downloaded onto a computer for enhancement or manipulation in an **image-editing program**. Digital cameras don't use films and you can instantly view the images. Illustrators and graphic artists often use digital cameras to create images for advertising brochures and instruction manuals.

Digital video camera

Records moving pictures in digital form. This can then be downloaded onto a computer or recorded onto videotape. **Video digitiser** converts film or video into computer files.

Flatbed scanner

A scanner electronically converts (digitises) a paper-based image into a computer file.

Drawings, **photographs** and **text** can be scanned in full colour. Optical Character Recognition (OCR) software converts scanned text into text files.

OUTPUT DEVICES
Monitor (Visual Display Unit or VDU)

Modern monitors can display **high-resolution** colour images (up to 1600 × 1200 pixels [screen dots]). These images are **clear, detailed** and **accurate**. The bigger the monitor, the more work can be seen at the same time. 17" is a minimum useful size for a monitor.

Flatbed plotter

This device produces **medium quality output**. Paper sizes are limited by bed size. **Coloured pens** are changed automatically as required. Special plotter paper can be expensive to buy. Flatbed plotters are quite noisy in use and are really only useful for **CAD line drawings**.

Drum plotter

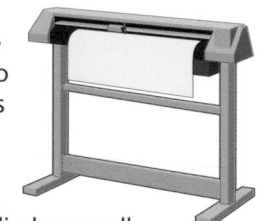

Drum plotters are used in industry to produce drawings on the **largest drawing sheets** available, A0 size. The paper is supplied on a roll which is moved back and forth to provide one axis of movement while the pen carriage moves from side to side giving the second axis of movement.

Both flatbed and drum plotters are commonly used in the engineering and building industries to produce **CAD line drawings**. Advances in technology mean that pen-based plotters are now being replaced by ink-jet-based plotters.

Ink-jet printer

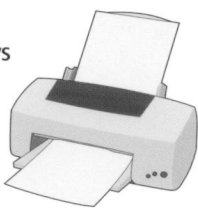

An ink-jet printer sprays a jet of ink onto the page to form text or graphics. The **print quality** is usually **very good** and they are not too expensive to buy. The **running costs can be high**, especially if you are printing colour graphics. Some ink-jets are reasonably quiet when printing but are **slow**. Industry often uses large (A0 size) ink-jet printers.

Laser printer

Laser printers produce **very high quality output** (600 dots per inch or better). They are much **faster** and **cheaper to run** than ink-jet printers. However, laser printers (especially A3 and colour models) are more expensive to buy than ink-jet printers.

OTHER DEVICES
Modem

A modem is both an input and an output device. See pages 43 and 44 for details.

Fax

Fax machines are used to send and receive images. A hand-drawn or pre-printed page is fed through the sending fax machine which scans the page and converts this image into a phone signal. The receiving fax machine converts this signal back into an image and prints it. A computer equipped with a fax modem can be used to send images directly to a fax machine without having to print the image first.

CAG – THE INFLUENCE OF CAG SYSTEMS ON INDUSTRY AND SOCIETY

INTRODUCTION

Computers have largely replaced drawing boards in industry and commerce. A CAG system of drawing offers many advantages over the traditional drawing board method.

ADVANTAGES OF A CAG SYSTEM OVER A DRAWING BOARD

Storage and retrieval

A completed drawing or series of drawings can be stored on hard drive, floppy disc, Zip disc or CD-R. These formats require less storage space than paper drawings. The drawings can then be printed as many times as required with no deterioration in quality.

Ease of modification

Companies who use CAG systems have advantages over competitors who rely on more traditional methods of modifying drawings. The ease and speed with which modifications can be made reduce time and costs, which in turn increases productivity.

Repetitive elements (library)

Drawings can contain a number of repetitive elements such as doors, windows, kitchen fittings and appliances. It is useful to have these items stored in a CAD library file. CAD library files are available for mechanical engineering, architecture and electronics. Items that you design need only be drawn once, saved to a library file, then retrieved and positioned each time they are required on a drawing. This saves time and effort, which increases productivity.

Drawing speed and drawing quality

It does take a considerable amount of time and financial investment by companies to train their CAG operators. In relative terms, however, drawing production is much faster using CAG than using traditional methods, so the company will save time and money in the long run. The quality of printed drawings is also much higher when using CAG.

Standardisation of drawings

Standardisation of drawings is often determined by drawing standards such as BSI. Standardisation of drawing layouts and styles can easily be created in the 'in-house' or corporate style adopted by the operator or the company.

Drawing size and flexibility

Drawings can be enlarged or reduced with no loss of detail. Extremely fine, detailed work can be produced using commands such as ZOOM. Positive location tools such as GRID, GRID SNAP and ATTACH enable accuracy to be maintained even in the smallest details.

HOMEWORK TASK 1

Which output devices would be used for:
1. sending electronic data long distances over a phone line?
2. producing hard copies of a large line drawing?
3. producing best quality colour prints?

COSTS AND OTHER IMPLICATIONS OF BUYING A CAG SYSTEM

The initial costs of buying computer systems and appropriate software can be an expensive outlay for companies. Another major factor is the retraining of staff who may have spent a lifetime producing drawings by traditional methods. A great deal of time can be taken up converting existing paper drawings to computer drawings, although new scanning tools have made this task much easier.

Before investing in a new computer system, a company must evaluate its needs. Some of the questions a company must answer are:
- what type of work will the computer system be used for (e.g. CAD, DTP, word processing, data management, 3-D modelling)?
- what types of software are needed?
- what size of computer system would be best (e.g. desktop PCs or workstations)?
- is a network required?
- if the company manufactures goods, can the manufacturing process be controlled using computers (**CAD/CAM**)?

MORE INFO

Make sure you learn and remember the following terms:
- **CAG** (computer-aided graphics) encompasses CAD, illustration, desktop publishing and 3-D CAD modelling.
- **CAD/CAM** (computer-aided design and manufacture) uses computers in both design and manufacture of products.

SOCIAL IMPLICATIONS

Computers and the use of advanced computer graphics have significantly improved our quality of life. For example, cinema and TV special effects and computer game graphics have become very realistic and absorbing.

This computer awareness has crept into our lives very quietly. On a day-to-day basis, most people readily accept that the computer is an essential tool which is used to advance medical research, save lives, and introduce new technologies into industry.

Traditional employment has seen tremendous change since the introduction of these new technologies. CAD/CAM has reduced the need for a great number of skilled and semi-skilled workers. Jobs which were traditionally done by skilled manual workers are now being overseen by fewer workers who operate and maintain automated machines and industrial robots which perform the manual work.

HOMEWORK TASK 2

1. Why is it important to back-up files?
2. Which input device would you use to convert a colour sketch into a computer file?
3. Name four types of discs used to store computer files.

CAG – COMPUTER-AIDED DRAWING (CAD)

2-D CAD

Computer-aided drawing (CAD) was developed so that architects and design engineers, who previously produced drawings on paper, could produce the same types of drawing on computers.

There are enormous benefits in using a CAD system instead of a drawing board system (see page 47).
- drawing aids such as grids, grid snap, ortho and zoom make the drawing process easier to control and help ensure that the drawing is accurate
- editing commands such as scale, fillet, break, trim and copy allow modifications to be made at any stage of the drawing process
- data from computer-aided drawings can be sent directly to machines to control manufacture (CAD/CAM).

3-D CAD MODELLING

The development of 3-D modelling software enables architects and designers to create 3-D models of their designs. Previously, 3-D models had to be 'built' from materials such as card, clay and polystyrene blocks.

Advantages of 3-D computer modelling over traditional 'built' models:
- can be produced much more quickly
- can be modified very quickly
- enable the designer to try colours and surface textures
- can be used to test structural designs before they are built, e.g. bridges and buildings
- can be realistically rendered
- are easily sent to remote locations
- take up less storage space than 'built' models
- can be used to create realistic simulations and games.

CAD DRAWING CLASSIFICATIONS

The following terms describe the common types of computer-aided drawings:
- **2-D** – orthographic projection in which each view shows only two dimensions
- **$2\frac{1}{2}$-D** – isometric, planometric, oblique and perspective views which show all three dimensions (length, breadth and height) on a pictorial drawing
- **3-D** – a 3-D computer model is a 'virtual object' which can be rotated on screen to be viewed from any angle.

GENERAL FEATURES OF A 2-D CAD PACKAGE (E.G. AUTOSKETCH® V2.1)
- uses xy co-ordinate system
- can create 2-D orthographic projections and $2\frac{1}{2}$-D (isometric, planometric, oblique and perspective) drawings
- incorporates layer system of constructing drawings (see page 66)

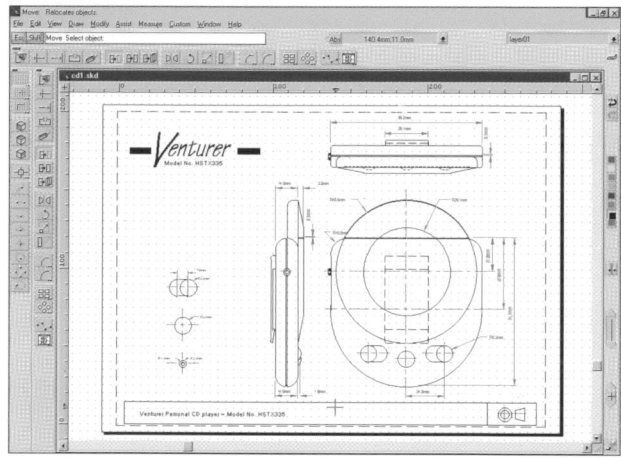

GENERAL FEATURES OF A 3-D CAD/ MODELLING PACKAGE (E.G. AUTOCAD 2000)
- uses xyz co-ordinate system
- automatically generates orthographic views from 3-D model
- rendering features can create tonal effects and surface textures
- models can be rotated and viewed from any angle

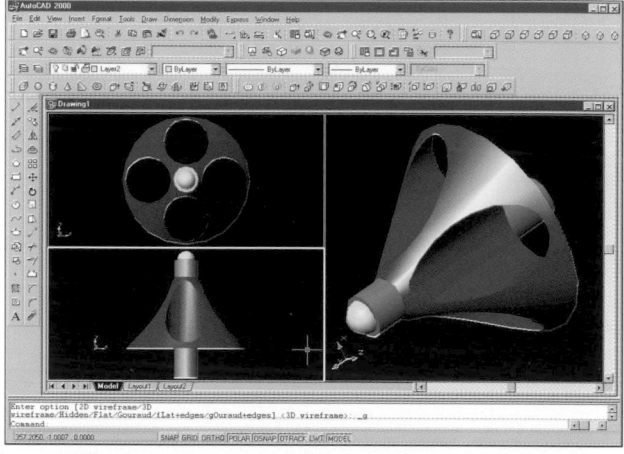

MORE INFO ABOUT 3-D MODELLING

There are three types of 3-D computer models:
- **wireframe model** – the object is built up using a series of connected lines

- **surface model** – the 3-D model is built up by drawing the surfaces of an object

- **solid model** – the 3-D model is built up using simple geometric forms such as cones, cylinders, prisms and cuboids. These can be added or subtracted to produce complex 3-D models.

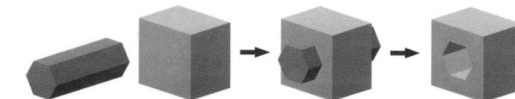

3-D models can be viewed in either wireframe or surface-rendered (shaded) form:
- **wireframe** – the object is represented by a series of lines. This image can be simplified by removing lines that are hidden.

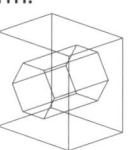 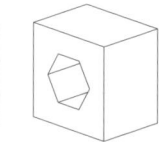

- **surface-rendered** (**shaded**) – the object is rendered with a solid-looking surface. Colours, shading and textures can be added to produce realistic-looking images.

3-D computer models can be rotated on screen and viewed from any angle.

INTRODUCTION

Some of the most useful functions found in CAD software are shown below. They all help to improve accuracy and drawing speed. You will need to use these functions in your CAD portfolio work. You must also learn and remember the information on pages 43 to 50 and pages 66 to 71 to prepare you for the KI questions in your exam.

ortho/isometric grid

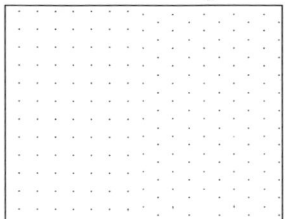

displays an on-screen grid of any given spacing. Makes orthographic and isometric drawing accurate and easier.

ortho

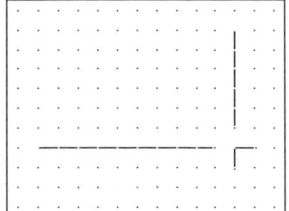

restricts cursor to horizontal and vertical movement only. This makes orthographic projection easier.

grid snap/grid lock

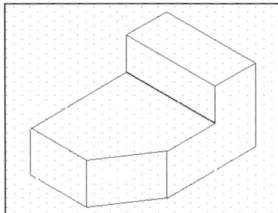

locates the start and end points of lines on a preset snap spacing. Improves accuracy.

library

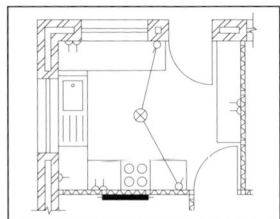

stores common drawing parts (icons) that can be added to drawings as often as required. Saves time and effort.

layers

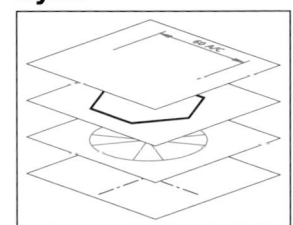

a drawing can be built up in several layers (like clear film overlays) which are switched on and off to make it easier to work on and understand.

zoom

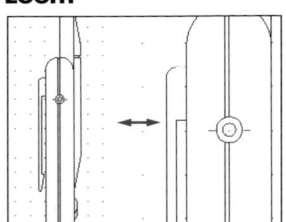

enlarges on-screen view so that small details appear bigger and are much easier to work on

line types

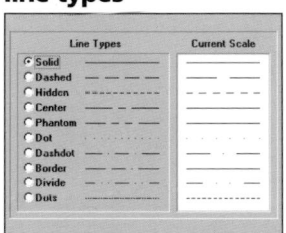

selects BSI line types used in all types of CAD drawing

rubber-banding/stretch

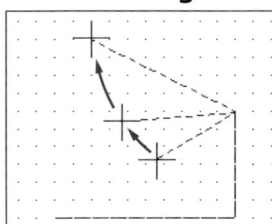

allows you to pull/stretch one end of a line or object across the screen

box/circle/arc

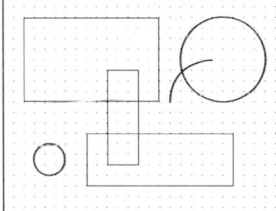

draws squares, rectangles, circles and arcs quickly and accurately

auto-dimensioning

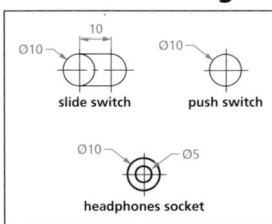

CAD software calculates and displays dimensions quickly and accurately to British Standards.

copy

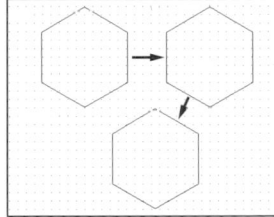

copies and positions objects without having to redraw them each time

ring and box arrays

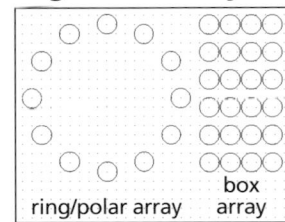

creates circular or rectangular arrangements of copied objects

fillet and chamfer

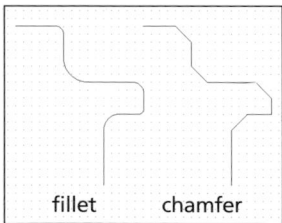

rounds (fillets) corners; angles (chamfers) corners

tangent

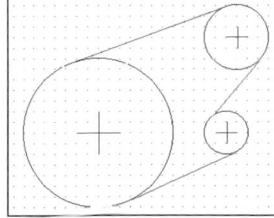

connects circles and lines at tangents

break, trim and extend

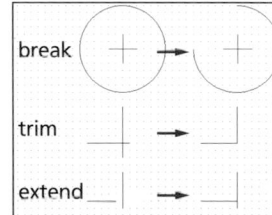

removes a section from the middle of a line; trims the end off a line; makes a line longer

rotate

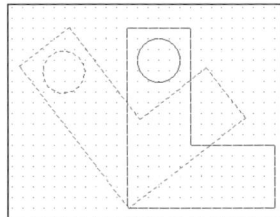

turns an object to any angle

scale

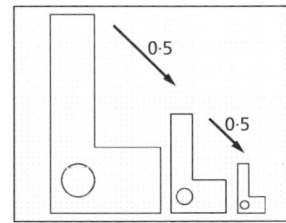

changes the size of objects

mirror (reflect)

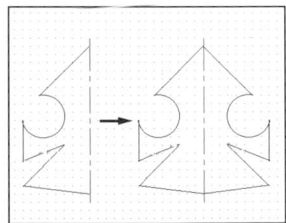

creates a mirror-image copy of an object

WORD PROCESSING

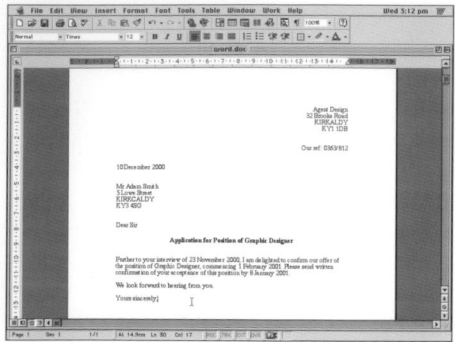

Word processing packages are used for inputting and editing text. They are used to produce a wide range of text documents – e.g. home and business letters, mailing lists, reports and manuals – and to prepare text for use in books, magazines and newsletters.

Word processors contain many features that help users to produce professional-looking documents quickly and accurately. The main features of a typical word processing package are:

- text can be **added**, **deleted**, **altered** or **moved**. **Search** and **replace** can also be used to locate and alter specific words or text automatically.
- a **spellchecker** – checks a document for misspelled words. Some word processing packages also have a grammar checker and a thesaurus.
- **text formatting** (**styling**) – changing the font (typeface), size, alignment, line spacing or colour.
- **page formatting** – allows user to set **margins**, number of **columns**, **headers** and **footers**, page numbering and **tab indents**
- **tables** and **graphics** can be included in the text.

SPREADSHEETS

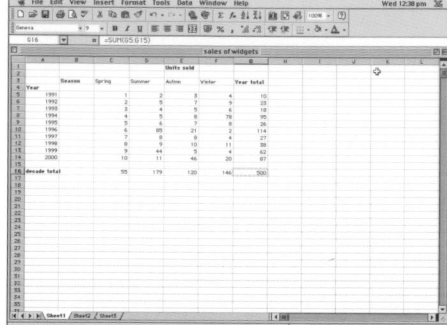

Spreadsheet packages are used for inputting and automatically calculating tables of numbers. Alterations can be made quickly and easily: if one number is changed, the application recalculates other values automatically and accurately.

Before electronic spreadsheets were introduced, tables of figures had to be calculated manually. This was very tedious and time-consuming. If just one piece of data was miscalculated and had to be edited, all of the previous work had to be redone!

Spreadsheets are mainly used to:

- automatically calculate **tables of numbers**
- produce **financial reports**
- produce **graphs** and **charts** for presentations.

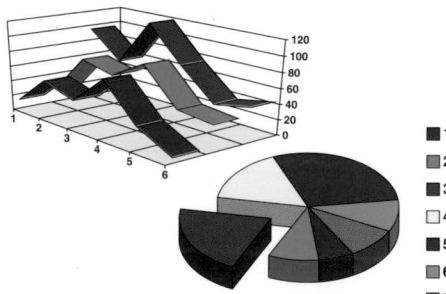

ILLUSTRATION

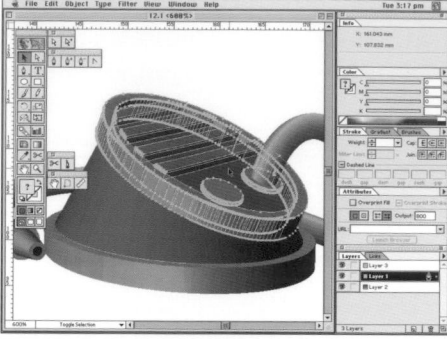

Illustration packages can be used to add colour, tone and texture to CAD drawings, as well as to create new drawings from scratch. Complex illustrations can be created and changed easily. Illustrations are an important part of design for books and advertising, TV/movie animation and computer games.

The main features of a typical illustration package are:

- **drawing tools** – enable users to alter existing drawings or create new ones
- **colour-mixing tools** – allow users to create their own colours
- **line styles** – different colours and thicknesses can be applied to lines
- **fill styles** – flat colours, patterns and colour gradients can be used to render drawings, creating realistic surface tones and textures
- **grids**, **guides**, **snap** and **rulers** – used for accurate drawing and editing
- **autotracing** – converts images from other types of programs, e.g. CAD software, for rendering in the illustration package.

DESKTOP PUBLISHING

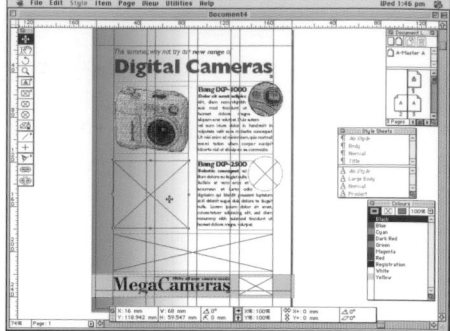

DTP packages are used to create publications such as newsletters, brochures, magazines and books by combining text and images (graphics) from other sources. They contain a wide range of powerful functions allowing very complex page layouts to be created quickly and accurately.

The main features of a typical DTP package are:

- **importing** of text and graphics from a wide range of sources, e.g. word-processed text, spreadsheets, scanned photographs, illustrations and clipart
- **precise positioning** – text and graphics are contained in separate **frames** for accurate positioning on the page (including scaling and rotating)
- powerful **text formatting and styling**. Dynamic and exciting effects for titles and other text can easily be created.
- **colour-mixing tools** – allow users to create their own colours
- **page formatting** – allows user to set **margins**, number of **columns**, **headers** and **footers** (including page numbering) and **tab indents**
- **guides**, **snap** and **rulers**
- automatic wrapping of text around graphics (**'text wrap'**).

INTRODUCTION

The third part of your course is called *Illustration and Presentation*. At your school or college, this may be known as your portfolio. During your course you will produce a collection of graphics and a card model and present them as your IP portfolio. Your portfolio is assessed in school and may also be sent to the SQA where the marking is carefully checked.

In your portfolio, you must demonstrate your skill in ten topics. The checklist below gives the title of each topic and the number of examples you should include in your portfolio.

Topic	No. of examples	Topic	No. of examples
PORTFOLIO CHECKLIST			
2-D and 3-D Graphs and Charts	2	Modelling	1
Use of Colour (Selection and Application)	3	Computer-aided Draughting	2
Use of Shading, Toning and Rendering	3	Use of a CAD Library	1
Layout and Lettering	3	CAG for Display	1
Display	1	Draughtsmanship across the Portfolio	*

* Each piece of work you include will be assessed for draughtmanship, i.e. neatness and accuracy in drawing, sketching, cutting and pasting.

Your teacher will lead you through your portfolio. Your portfolio may be different to the examples shown in this book but the skills and techniques used will be the same. Pages 52 to 71 give examples of portfolio graphics which have been assessed at Credit level grade 1. You should strive to achieve the standards of design and technique set here. Detailed notes explain how each graphic was designed and produced.

During your course you must create your own graphics. Do not simply copy other people's ideas. Your own creative input is important and your design and layout skills will be assessed in several topics.

PORTFOLIO ASSESSMENT

Each of the ten topics is graded individually. In each topic, the grade awarded will be your **best** grade in that topic. For example, if you produce three pieces of work for Layout and Lettering at grades 4, 2 and 1 respectively, your grade for that topic will be grade 1. The topic grades are then added up and divided by 10 to give an average grade. This will be your grade for *Illustration and Presentation*.

MAKING BEST USE OF YOUR TIME

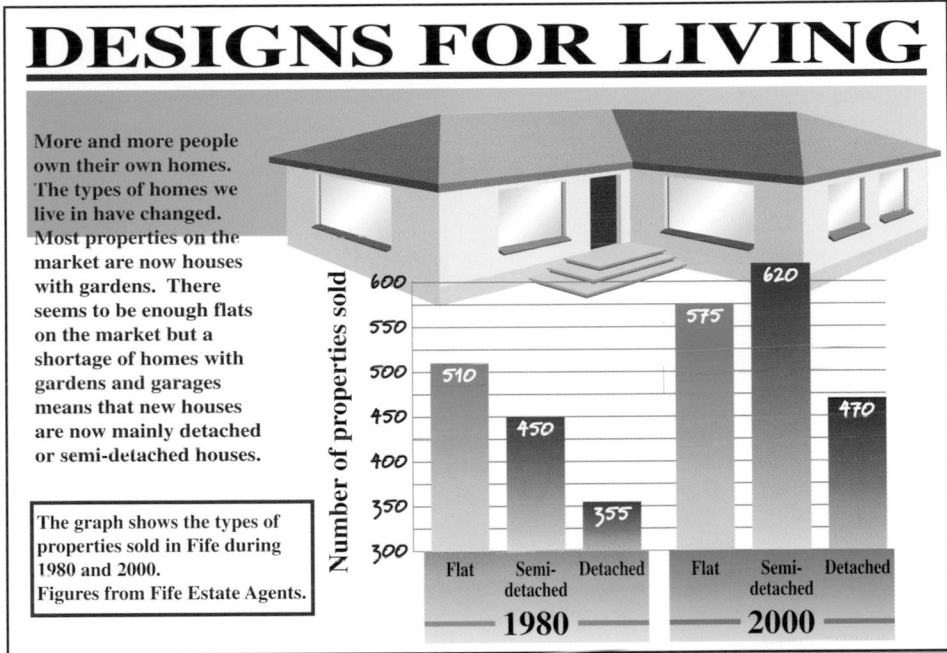

DESIGNS FOR LIVING

More and more people own their own homes. The types of homes we live in have changed. Most properties on the market are now houses with gardens. There seems to be enough flats on the market but a shortage of homes with gardens and garages means that new houses are now mainly detached or semi-detached houses.

The graph shows the types of properties sold in Fife during 1980 and 2000. Figures from Fife Estate Agents.

Do not be misled by the number of graphics which you have to produce for each topic. Your aim should be to cover the required number of topics with **as few graphics as possible**. For example, the bar graph shown above can be used for assessment in the following topics:
- 2-D and 3-D Graphs and Charts
- Use of Colour (colour selection only)
- Layout and Lettering
- Display
- Computer-aided Draughting
- CAG for Display
- Draughtsmanship

As you can see, this one graphic covers seven of the ten portfolio topics. In this way you can reduce the number of graphics in your portfolio and spend more time improving the quality of each piece.

The order in which you tackle the portfolio graphics will vary from school to school. Your teacher will have planned this carefully. The order in this book is roughly the same as in the checklist, and not necessarily the order in which you will do them.

LAYOUT AND LETTERING, DISPLAY AND CAG FOR DISPLAY

INTRODUCTION

Layout and Lettering, Display and CAG for Display are topics which test your creativity and your graphic design skills. They can all be considered together. You will probably use the same graphics for assessment in all three topics.

Graphs and Charts is the other topic which tests your creativity. Your graphs and charts will also be assessed in Layout and Lettering, Display and CAG for Display.

In these topics you will design graphic displays which have three main parts: an **illustration**, some **text** and a **background**.

To produce effective graphic displays you must consider the following: contrast, harmony, position, balance, unity, dominance, depth, flow and colour.

Examples and advice on layout and display are given throughout this section. It is useful at this stage to learn some basic design tips for producing graphic displays.

TIPS

- Keep the display simple – too many parts are difficult to organise. Don't use too many colours.
- Avoid bold diagonal lines – they can easily dominate a graphic.
- Connect the parts in some way – by overlapping them or using an **accent colour**, for example. (An accent colour is a colour which is used in several different parts of a graphic. Your eye picks out this colour, helping to unify the graphic. An accent colour usually contrasts with one of the main colours.)
- Give the illusion of depth by suggesting a foreground and background.
- Create contrast of colour, tone, style or depth to make a graphic more eye-catching.
- Balance the picture. Text can be used as a visual element as well as to give information.
- Decide what the most important parts are and make sure they dominate the graphic.
- Try positioning your illustration off-centre. This changes the focus of the page and gives the graphic visual impact. It also leaves more useful space for text.

HOW TO KEEP IT SIMPLE

- The bottle overlaps all three background areas. This helps unify the graphic and makes it feel organised.
- Having the bottle in front gives the impression of depth.
- Horizontal lines are easy on the eye.
- The background colours are very strong. These might have dominated the graphic, but the tones and colours of the bottle are strong enough to compete.
- The crisp highlights on the bottle provide eye-catching contrast against the dark background.

CONTRAST AND COLOUR UNITY

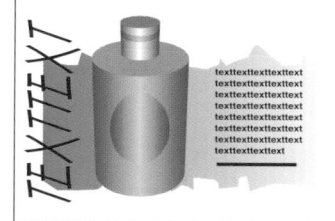

- The green background makes a strong, eye-catching contrast with the red detail on the bottle.
- The red accent colour is used on the bottle, in the text at the top and in the line at the bottom. Your eye picks out this accent colour, helping to unify the graphic.
- There are strong connections between all the parts of this graphic, providing unity and balance.

FLASHBARS

- The band of colour in the background is called a flashbar. It is the simplest type of backdrop and can be rectangular or irregular. It pushes the bottle forward – this is called 'dominance' – and creates unity by connecting the other parts together.
- The ragged edge of the flashbar contrasts with the formal geometric shape of the bottle.

LESS IS MORE

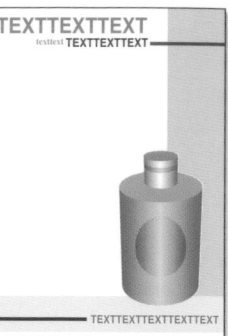

- This graphic incorporates lots of white space.
- The pale background colours help to focus attention on the product.
- The text is placed in lines across the page to create interest and give balance to the graphic.
- Red is the accent colour. Green text provides contrast.
- The whole graphic has a sophisticated look, suggesting an up-market product.

AN EXAMPLE OF POOR LAYOUT AND DISPLAY

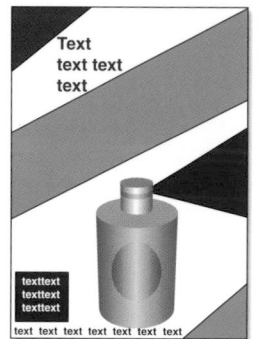

- There are nine unconnected parts. This looks disorganised and lacks unity.
- Bold diagonal lines dominate the page.
- The bottle should be dominant but is lost among bold background shapes and colours.
- There is no focal point.
- Too many colours fragment the picture. There is no colour balance – neither contrast nor harmony.
- The bottle has been positioned in the centre. This leaves awkward spaces to fill down either side.

HOMEWORK TASK

Select a colour advertisement from a magazine which displays a product. Analyse its layout and display by answering the following questions:
- Why has the product been placed in its position in the poster?
- Why have the background colours been chosen?
- How has the graphic designer tied all the parts together to create a unified picture?
- Has the graphic designer created depth in the poster? How has this been achieved?

2-D AND 3-D GRAPHS AND CHARTS – BASICS

INTRODUCTION

Statistics are part of our everyday lives. Sales figures, government spending, sports league tables and retail price increases are all areas in which facts and figures change frequently. Such information can be very complex and difficult to understand. Graphs and charts make statistics more visual. Turning facts and figures into graphics can highlight important parts and make the information much easier to understand.

There are four main types of graphs and charts: pie chart, bar chart, line graph and table. You must select the right type when designing your own graphs.

PIE CHART

A pie chart is usually shown as a circle. This circle represents the 'complete' or 'whole' number and is divided into segments by lines running from the centre. Each segment forms part of the whole number.

Use:
• to display parts of a 'whole number'.

Do not use:
• when there are too many segments or if some slices will be very thin
• a shape which is too difficult to divide up accurately. The shape does not need to be a circle but must divide up simply and accurately.

BAR CHART

A bar chart can be a row of bars showing how values vary over a period of time, or a row of bars showing how different values compare with one another.

Use:
• when you want to highlight individual figures rather than show an overall flow of figures
• when comparing different items or figures.

Do not use:
• when too many bars are required. This would make the chart difficult to follow.
• when the overall flow of figures is more important than individual values – use a line graph instead.

THE WORLD HONEY MARKET

USA 20%
Argentina 5%
Mexico 15%
Russia 35%
China 25%

The market has 5 main producers.

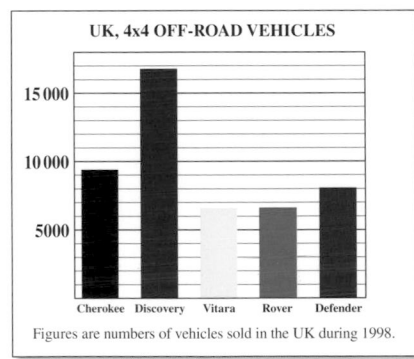

UK, 4x4 OFF-ROAD VEHICLES

Cherokee Discovery Vitara Rover Defender

Figures are numbers of vehicles sold in the UK during 1998.

LINE GRAPH

A line graph is often used to show quantities plotted over a period of time. The x-axis (horizontal scale) represents time. The y-axis (vertical scale) represents the quantities. The line/curve is then plotted on a grid.

Use:
• when it is important to show the changes of figures over time.

Do not use:
• when some quantities are tiny and others are huge (use a table instead).

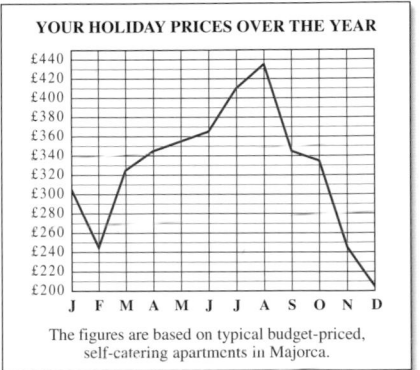

YOUR HOLIDAY PRICES OVER THE YEAR

J F M A M J J A S O N D

The figures are based on typical budget-priced, self-catering apartments in Majorca.

TABLE

A table displays numbers or words arranged into rows and columns. A spreadsheet is a computerised table which can be used to calculate data. It can also produce graphs and charts.

Use:
• when the individual figures, rather than the overall flow, are most important
• when comparing numbers which are too far apart to be shown on a chart
• when presenting large amounts of very precise information.

Do not use:
• when you can use one of the other three types.

Participation in the most popular sporting activities
How our leisure time has changed in 30 years

	1970			2000		
	M	F	Total	M	F	Total
Swimming	12%	10%	11%	18%	18%	18%
Snooker (and Pool)	6%	0%	3%	22%	2%	12%
Aerobics	0%	0%	0%	1%	9%	5%
Golf	4%	1%	2·5%	8%	1%	4·5%
Jogging	1%	0%	0·5%	8%	2%	5%
Football	3%	0%	1·5%	8%	0%	4%
Cycling	2%	0%	1%	4%	2%	3%

The types of graphs and charts shown on this page are used in newspapers, magazines, brochures and on television. They generally accompany an article or story, often with a supporting picture or graphic. Your graphs and charts must be self-explanatory and stand alone without an accompanying story or article. In order to achieve this you must include a short note to help make the information clear.

The graphs and charts shown on this page are in basic form and would only be awarded Foundation level grades as they have not been graphically enhanced to support the subject matter. Page 54 demonstrates how the graphs and charts on this page can be enhanced to Credit level.

INTRODUCTION

You need to include two graphs or charts in your portfolio. They should each be of a different type, and at least one of them must include some computer work. They can be either 2-D or 3-D. Each graph or chart should either be combined ('built-in') with a graphic, or separate and positioned next to or on top of the graphic.

WHAT MAKES A COMPLETE GRAPH?

Every graph should have:
• a 'snappy' and explicit title
• a short note to help make the information clear
• a graphic to support the subject matter and improve the presentation
• a pie chart, bar chart, line graph or table to display the statistics.

WHAT MAKES A CREDIT LEVEL GRAPH?

To achieve Credit level, a graph must also:
• be the correct type to display your chosen information
• be graphically enhanced to support the subject matter
• be complete, with no vital parts missing
• demonstrate a high standard of presentation (i.e. the layout, text, graph and graphic enhancement must be of a high quality).

If everything is in place, the graph should be clear, easy to understand and have visual impact.

The graphs on this page have been taken from page 53 and enhanced to Credit level, grade 1 standard.

The layout of graph, text and graphic is important if the overall design is to have visual impact. Colour can be used to unify the design or introduce eye-catching contrast.

When you are designing a graph, it is important to be aware of the different media you can use. The graphs on this page were produced using a variety of different media. The notes below each graph explain why.

PIE CHART

Coloured pencils, which are quick and easy to control, are used for the combined graph and honey pot. A computer is used to produce high-quality text and background colour. The bees are clipart and are sized and positioned to help give the graphic depth.

BAR CHART

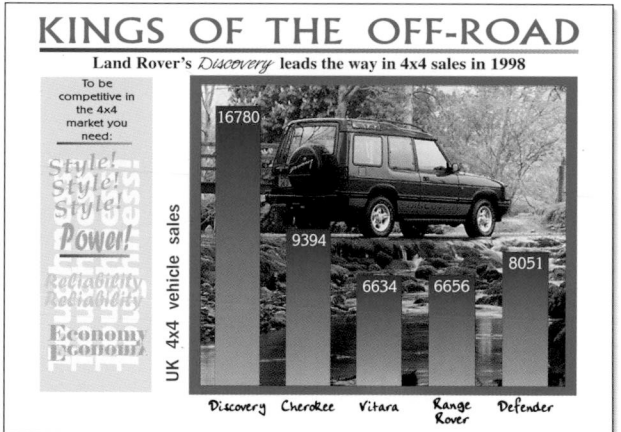

Found materials, such as photographic images from magazines and newspapers, can be cut and pasted to enhance the graph; here a picture of a vehicle is used. The text and graph are computer-generated and carefully cut and pasted onto the magazine picture.

LINE GRAPH

The entire graphic is made from coloured card, a useful medium which is easy to use and provides immediate colour and texture. The text is computer-generated and the figures are clipart. The graph has been combined with the holiday theme to make the information more visual.

TABLE

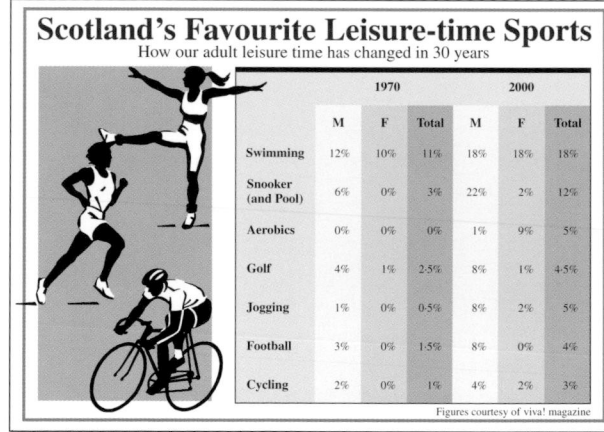

The table is made using spreadsheet software by typing in the text and figures. The purple flashbar picks out the purple in the table and helps to unify the graphic. The clipart figures support the subject matter and have been positioned carefully to create visual impact.

INTRODUCTION

This page takes you through the process of creating a graph step by step.

WORKED EXAMPLE

1. Select a topic and find data.

- Select a topic which interests you. Avoid the obvious choices such as pocket money or who gets the bus to school and who walks.
- Books of statistics, such as *UK Social and Business Data* or *The Usborne Book of Facts and Lists*, are useful sources of information. Your teacher will have some of these books and so will your local library.
- Make a note of the facts and figures you require.

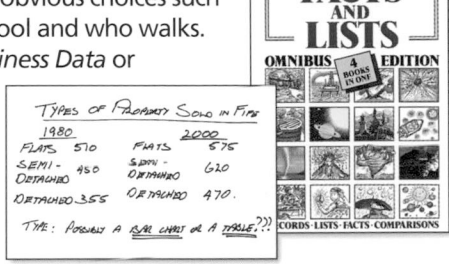

2. Design your own graph.

- Carefully choose the correct type of graph. This example uses a bar chart.
- Sketch out a few design ideas. Remember, try both methods: a graph which is combined with the enhancements and a separate graph with enhancements beside it.
- Be sure nothing is missing. Your graph should have a title, a graphic to support the topic, a short note to clarify what the graph is about and the graph itself.
- Write out the text now to save time later.

3. Choose the best mediums.

- Select which mediums you are going to use: hand-drawn, CAD, clipart, found materials or card. (Remember, you must have computer input in one of your graphs.) In this example, CAD is used.
- Since this house has been drawn using a computer, it can also be assessed in the topic *Computer-aided Draughting*.
- The first task is to draw the house using CAD software (pages 68 to 69 show how the house is drawn).
- This line drawing is then imported into an illustration package (e.g. Designworks) where colour and tone can be added.

4. Complete the graph.

- Decide how you are going to draw the graph itself. This graph has been drawn using an illustration package and is made up of lines and boxes with coloured fills.
- You might want to use specialised graph software for this, or you might prefer to make it using coloured card. Either method is fine, so long as the quality of work is high.
- Combine all the parts in a balanced way. The bar graph is the most important part and is positioned at the front.
- Notice how the quantities begin at 300. This makes the differences between totals more obvious and keeps the graph a comfortable height.
- The green flashbar at the back helps push the house forward and connects the house and text. It also picks out the green in the bar graph creating unity.

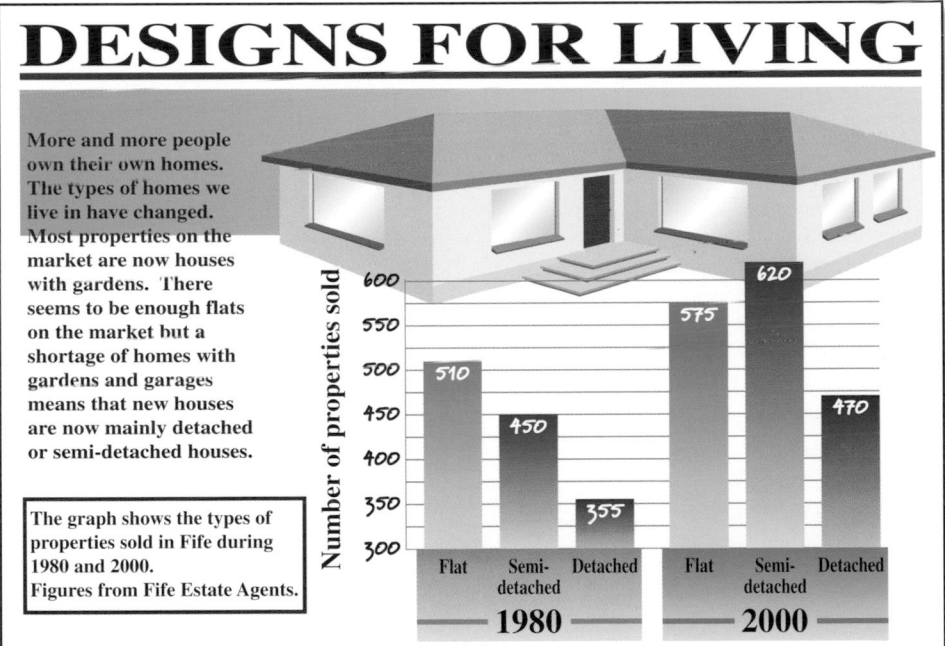

TIPS

- Experiment with background colours.
- Create contrast, e.g. by using red and green together.
- Introduce an accent colour to help tie all the parts together.

PORTFOLIO ASSESSMENT VALUES

Topic	Grade	Topic	Grade
Graphs & Charts	1	Modelling	
Use of Colour		CAD	1
Toning & Rendering		CAD Library	
Layout & Lettering	1	CAG Display	1
Display	1	Draughtsmanship	1

SHADING, TONING AND RENDERING BASICS

INTRODUCTION

This page explains the basic principles of shading, toning and rendering. These are important illustration skills which you will use to make your graphics exciting and realistic. The examples on this page have all been produced using coloured pencils. This is the medium you will use for most of your practice. You will need three examples of rendered work (each in a different medium) for your portfolio. Pages 57 to 63 show examples of rendering, layout and display in three mediums: coloured pencil, marker pens and chalk pastels. To improve your rendering skills, you should practise as much as possible. All the examples on this page are suitable practice pieces.

TONE BOXES

You will use two types of tone:
- **flat tone** for flat surfaces
- **graded tone** for curved surfaces.

Shading a tone box lets you practise applying tone. Always use a sharp, soft 2B or coloured pencil for shading. Make broad pencil strokes. Light tones need light pressure. Dark tones need more pressure and repeated strokes.

Shade flat tones in the following order: 1, 5, 3, 2, 4.

For graded tone, work from dark to light, easing pressure as you go.

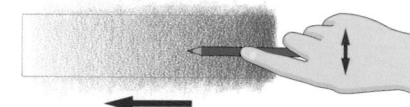

SHADING AND TONING

Shading and toning is used to make drawings and sketches look solid and give them form. This is done by understanding the effect that light has on the surfaces of an object.

RENDERING

Rendering takes shading and toning one stage further: it adds texture or pattern to surfaces suggesting a particular material or product.

Light source comes from over your left shoulder.

1. Top surface
Normally lightest, tone 1. Shade this surface **first** using yellow, then orange.

4. Texture
The wood grain is just a darker tone of the base colour, yellow/orange.

3. Side facing the light
Tone 3. Shade this side **last** using yellow, then orange.

2. Shadow side
Facing away from light, tone 5. Shade this surface **second** using yellow, then orange.

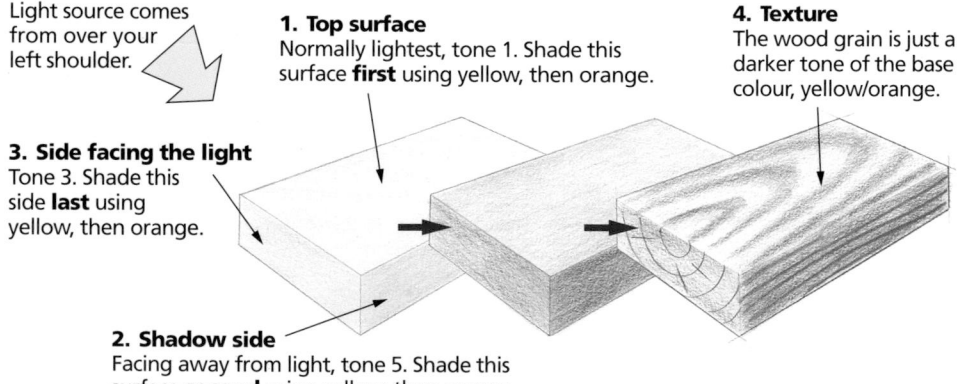

CURVED SURFACES

Rendering curved surfaces requires a little more skill. There are three main curved forms: cylinders, cones and spheres.

TIPS
- Decide which direction the light is coming from (in this case, top left).
- Work from dark to light.
- Place the highlight off-centre, facing the light source.

CONTRAST AND DETAIL

Contrast and detail make your illustrations more eye-catching.
- Pick out surface detail carefully in light and dark tones.
- Make dark tones as dark as possible without being shiny. Keep pale tones very light.
- Place highlights and dark tones close together to create contrast.
- Joins or gaps provide opportunity for dark shadows and crisp highlights.

SHINY METALLIC SURFACES

Shiny metallic surfaces can be rendered using a **desertscape**. Imagine the shiny object in a desert. It reflects the simple environment: blue sky, a sandy ground colour and a blue and black horizon line.

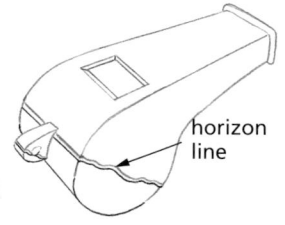

horizon line

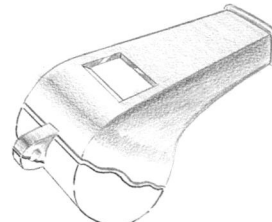

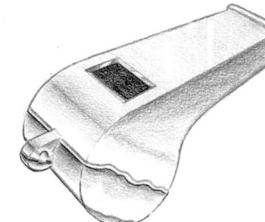

- Draw the outline in three colours. Add a blue and black horizon line.

- Add blue sky tones.

- Finish with sandy ground tones and detail.

COLOURED PENCILS – SHADING, TONING AND RENDERING

INTRODUCTION

This page explains the main stages in producing a finished illustration in coloured pencil, from choosing the colours through to the final rendered illustration. Pages 58 to 59 show how this illustration is displayed as part of an advertising graphic. It is useful to combine rendered pieces with layout and display. This helps reduce the amount of work you have to do and gives you more time to raise the quality of this work.

Your teacher will help you select a suitable subject for displaying your illustration skills. The following example is an illustration of a plastic cosmetics bottle. This product will be marketed to appeal to young men who play sport, so the design will use the theme of extreme sports, such as surfing, windsurfing, hang-gliding, sky-diving and snowboarding.

WORKED EXAMPLE

1. Design the shape and colour scheme of the bottle.

- Choose colours which appeal to the intended market (see pages 40 to 42 for more information about colour and colour schemes).
- Keep your design simple. Don't use too many colours. Rendering even a simple bottle in perspective is complex work. You gain no marks for the design of the bottle itself, so don't overdo it.

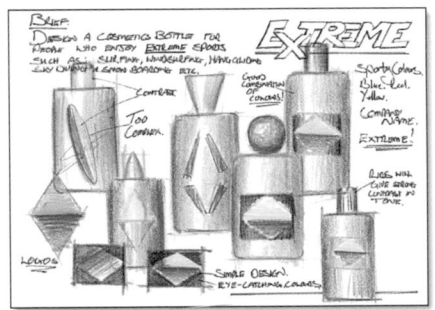

2. Sketch or draw the bottle shape.

- Begin with the ellipse at the top (**1**).
- Build up a line sketch or drawing. (Use a set square for straight lines and draw curves freehand.)
- The curves at the bottom are more rounded than those at the top. This gives a strong perspective appearance (**2**).
- The result should be a well-proportioned pencil lay-over of the bottle with rounded shoulders. (A lay-over is a tracing aid.)
- Trace over the pencil lay-over in colour. Do not line in the shoulders (**3**) – these will appear as uncoloured highlights.
- Note that a well-drawn bottle also provides evidence of good draughtmanship.

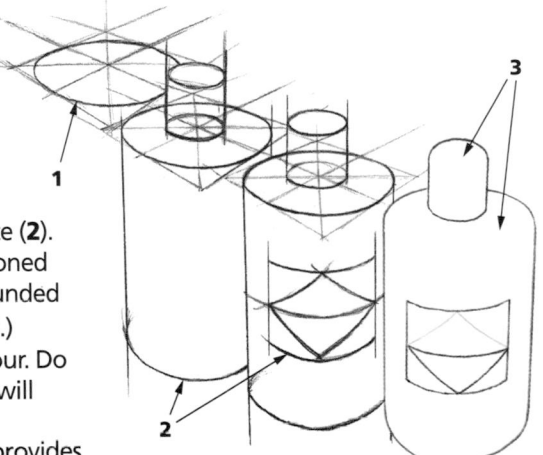

3. Render the bottle.

- In this example, the light source comes from over your left shoulder down onto the bottle.
- Apply the main colours.
- Do the flat, top surfaces first (use light tones).
- Avoid shading the shoulders on the bottle and cap. These will become highlights with no colour. This is the trickiest part of the work. If the highlights along the shoulder (**1**) and running down the bottle (**2**) are done well, your work will be graded at Credit level.
- Always work from dark to light, easing the pressure as you go.
- Take care when shading – the tones must fade gradually towards the highlights along the shoulder and down the bottle.

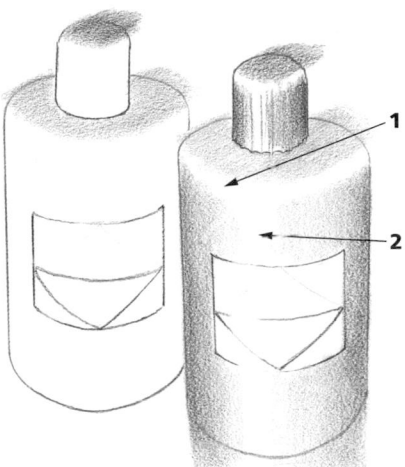

4. Add finishing touches.

- Detail and contrast will make the illustration sparkle.
- Add ribs to the cap to produce concave flutes (**1**). This creates additional contrast between light and dark.
- Add a shadow behind the cap to help give depth and contrast (**2**).
- Add the company logo. The tones must be carefully graded to match the bottle (**3**).
- Darken the bottom edge of the bottle. This rounded edge is in shade (**4**).
- Use the same effect on the back edges at the top of the bottle (**5**).

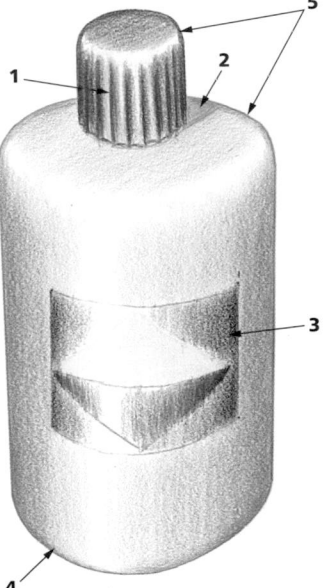

COLOURED PENCILS – LAYOUT AND DISPLAY

INTRODUCTION

Choosing a theme for your display can help make the display more exciting and also make the project more interesting. In the following example, the display is based around the subject of extreme sports in order to incorporate the excitement, movement and colours of surfing, windsurfing or hang-gliding.

The first task is finding source material: visit your local newsagent and check out your teacher's magazine collection and computer clipart. Decide what theme you want to use in your display and what sort of colour scheme you will use. In this case, a surfing magazine provides excellent backdrop material and dynamic surfing figures. A company name, 'extreme', has also been chosen.

WORKED EXAMPLE

1. Look for images and colours which you think will enhance your illustration.
- Check out various sources of material. In this case, a surfing magazine has been selected.

2. Choose colours.
- Cut the bottle out so it can be laid over backdrops to test the colour balance. In this example a blue surfing scene works best.
- Identify an accent colour. Here the red colour on the bottle is being used as an accent colour, so a picture of a surfer containing a small area of red has been selected.
- Remember, you will have to write a short report on your choice of colours.

3. Design the layout and text.
- Using your illustration and the backdrop as a starting point, sketch out several layouts which promote the company name and connect it with exciting sports.
- Choose a method for producing text – either look for existing text in magazines to cut and paste, or produce text yourself using coloured pencils or marker pens, or use a computer.
- Consider what you want to say, which styles of text to use (see page 59), what colours to select and how to position the text. Text can be an important, visual part of the display.
- In this example, computer-generated text is used to give a high-quality appearance. The company logo is produced using a formal-looking font, and the slogan is produced using an informal, freehand font to create contrast.

4. Bring it together by creating an effective layout.
- You need to **plan the layout** carefully.
- Sketch an actual-size layout on paper and measure the size of each part. Make sure the computer-generated text fits the space. In this case, there are five parts to our display, as shown below.

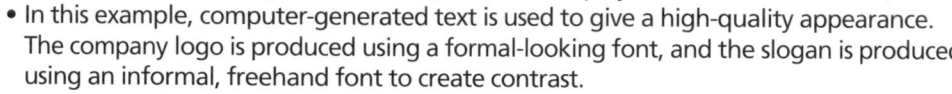
computer-generated logo

magazine backdrop

computer-generated backdrop

illustration

magazine figure

COLOURED PENCILS – LAYOUT AND DISPLAY (CONT.)

5. Evaluation of the layout and display.

- The overlapping parts – the bottle and the surfer – create depth and unity.
- The bottle appears to be closer to the viewer, making it the dominant feature.
- The blue and yellow strip down the left helps to connect the parts together vertically. The thin blue stripe behind the bottle ties the parts together horizontally.
- The quality of the finished production is extremely important. Cutting and pasting of the parts must be done neatly and accurately. This provides evidence of good draughtmanship.

PORTFOLIO ASSESSMENT VALUES

Topic	Grade	Topic	Grade
Graphs & Charts		Modelling	
Use of Colour	1	CAD	
Toning & Rendering	1	CAD Library	
Layout & Lettering	1	CAG Display	
Display	1	Draughtsmanship	1

MORE INFO ABOUT TEXT STYLES

When deciding which style(s) of text to use in your display, think about the type of look you are trying to create.

- For a **formal**, **traditional** look, use a font such as Times or Times New Roman.

- For a **formal**, **modern** look, use a font such as Arial or Helvetica.

- For an **informal**, **fun** look, use a font such as Comic Sans.

You can create contrast in your design by using more than one style of text. Contrast can also be created by using different sizes and weights of text together. For example:

10 point Times

18 point Arial Black

STAY FRESH STAY WILD

USE OF COLOUR

Assessment of Use of Colour is based on your selection **and** your manual application of colour. In your portfolio, you will use three manually-applied colour mediums: coloured pencil, marker pen and pastel. This manual colour work provides part of the evidence for Use of Colour. You must also write a colour theory report on one of your portfolio graphics to complete the evidence.

6. Write a colour theory report.

You must write a report for one of your graphic displays – choose the most suitable one – similar to the report shown below.

In your report you must identify where you have used warm, cold, advancing and receding colours and explain why you have chosen them. State where and why you have created contrast or harmony and where you have used an accent colour to create unity or contrast. Also mention how you have created the illusion of depth and how you have given a focus to the layout.

'Extreme' Cosmetics Bottle Colour Theory Report

I have used **'sporty' colours** – blue, red and yellow – for the bottle. Along with a small amount of grey, these are the only colours in the display. My colours are equally spaced on the colour wheel, making an **exciting scheme**.

The main background colour is blue which is a **receding colour** – it appears to be further away, suggesting distance or **depth**. The **accent colour**, red, appears in small details and **unifies the display**. Red is an **advancing colour** so it makes those details stand out.

Contrast is very important in creating an eye-catching display. I have used several different forms of contrast:
- **colour**, **warm** and **cool colours**, **tone**, **depth**
- **styles of text**
- **textures**
- **vertical** and **horizontal** lines
- a **stationary** bottle and a **moving** figure.

I have positioned the bottle **off-centre** to leave a good space for the slogan. The bottle's position also creates a **good balance** with the surfer, which is the other dominant part of the graphic.

The result is an exciting, balanced display with strong visual impact.

MARKER PENS – SHADING, TONING AND RENDERING

INTRODUCTION

During the development and presentation of ideas, designers need to use techniques and materials which are both quick and effective. Marker pens are ideal for this and are used in many areas of design development, including packaging, product design and fashion design.

Marker pens are available in a wide range of colours and several tip thicknesses and shapes. They are either water-based or spirit-based, with spirit-based pens offering a greater colour range.

To get the most from marker pens, it is important to use the correct materials and master some basic techniques. If you have not attempted marker rendering before, try doing the 'torch project' shown here.

The type of torch used here is available in most high street stores. It is a good exercise to sketch and measure it before making the line drawing shown in stage 1. Follow the stages step by step. Assume the light source is coming over your left shoulder.

WORKED EXAMPLE

1. Produce a line drawing.

- Start with an accurate, 1:1 scale, line drawing – measure the torch to find dimensions.
- Draw this directly onto **bleed-proof paper** using drawing instruments and coloured pencils which match your marker pens (use any two colours).
- The layout shows the torch drawn in different orthographic views. The red parts have been drawn separately.
- Extend the lines at the corners to provide a guide when you need to cut the shapes from the sheet. This will avoid problems if the outlines become obscured when applying the marker pens.

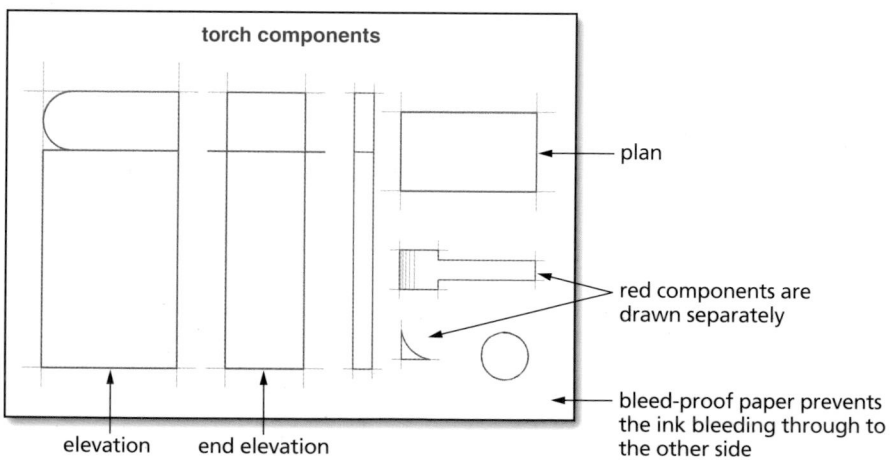

torch components

plan

red components are drawn separately

bleed-proof paper prevents the ink bleeding through to the other side

elevation   end elevation

2. Block in the colour.

- Using parallel strokes, apply the **base colour** in a **streaky** manner. This is achieved by each stroke slightly overlapping the previous one.
- Start and finish each stroke of the pen outside the shape being rendered. This is called the **strike-through** method.

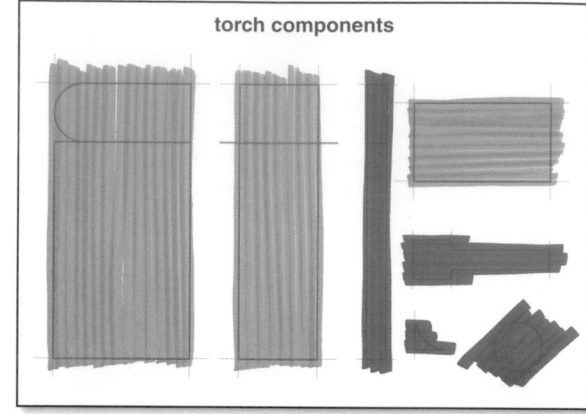

torch components

3. Add a reflective surface texture.

- Add random sweeps at an angle of approximately **60**°, working from the bottom-right corner towards the top-left.
- Space out the sweeps as you near the top-left corner. This creates a slightly reflective surface finish, simulating the texture of plastic.
- Repeat this for each component in turn, changing the colours as required.

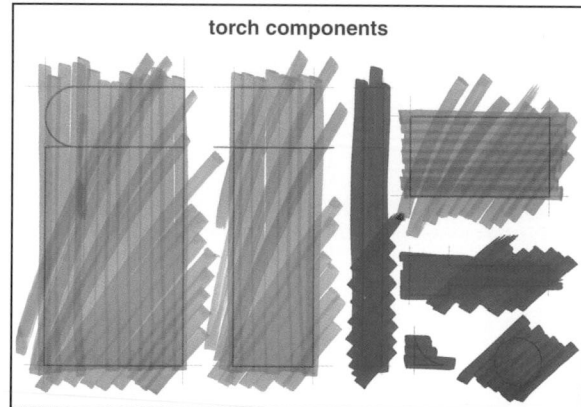

torch components

Note that neatness and accuracy throughout these steps also provide evidence of good draughtmanship.

MORE INFO

Use a **chiselled nib** to draw broad strokes.

Use a **bullet nib** for fine detail.

4. Add tone (shadows and highlights).

- When the first application of marker has dried, apply a **cool grey** to the two edges of the rounded casings which face away from the light source. This creates a shadow effect. Apply further shading using a black pencil.
- Opposite the 'shadow' edges are the two edges which face towards the light source. Lighten the tone here using a **soft** white pencil.

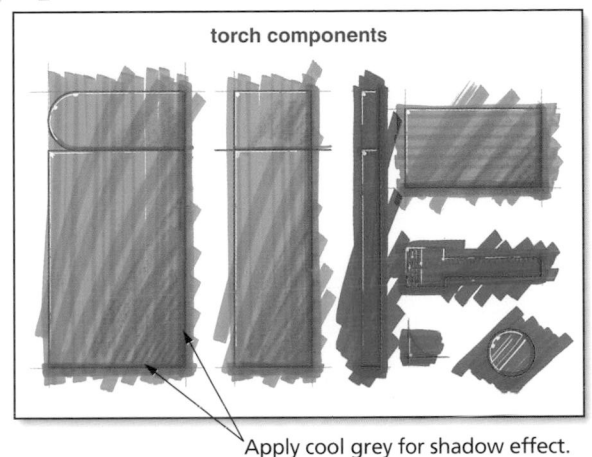

torch components

Apply cool grey for shadow effect.

5. Add detailing.

- Corners and edges which face towards the light source need highlights. These can be added with a sharp white pencil. There also tends to be a very bright highlight where two or more edges come together. This is called a **'farkle'** and can be applied as a dot of white gouache paint or correction fluid.
- For final presentation, cut out the component parts carefully using a craft knife, a safety rule and a cutting mat.
- A glue stick is useful when fixing the illustrations onto the paper.
- Further detailing can be applied using rub-down lettering and texture sheets.

6. Design the layout and text.

- Before finalizing the layout, try out several roughs of different text and backgrounds.
- Keep your layout simple – displaying two or three views can be difficult.
- Consider textured paper and computer-generated text. These are quick and effective.
- Refer to page 52 for further advice on designing your layout.

7. Evaluation of the layout and display.

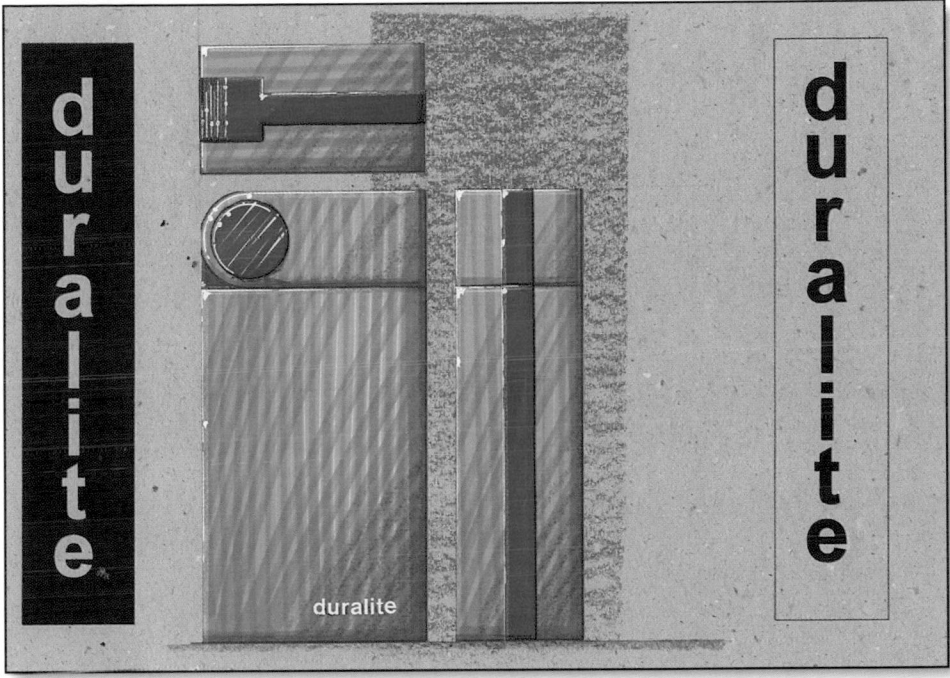

- The red/orange flashbar is produced with a coloured pencil. It pushes the illustration forward because it contrasts with the green of the torch. It also adds depth to the graphic and connects all three views of the torch.
- The three views of the torch have been positioned off-centre to make the graphic more interesting.
- The text on one side of the graphic is the 'negative' of the text on the opposite side. This adds contrast to the overall display.
- The main backdrop is provided by a coloured/textured paper. This provides a contrast to the shiny 'plastic' rendering of the torch.
- The ground line suggests that there is a solid base under the torch, which in turn makes the torch look solid.

TIP

If using round or square buttons in your design, why not use self-adhesive dots or squares?

PORTFOLIO ASSESSMENT VALUES

Topic	Grade	Topic	Grade
Graphs & Charts		Modelling	
Use of Colour	1	CAD	
Toning & Rendering	1	CAD Library	
Layout & Lettering	1	CAG Display	
Display	1	Draughtsmanship	1

CHALK PASTELS – SHADING, TONING AND RENDERING

INTRODUCTION

Chalk pastels are a relatively inexpensive rendering material and can be used to complement coloured pencil and/or marker pen work.

It is important to note that rendering with chalk pastels needs advance planning and preparation. The procedure can be rather messy if care is not taken. **Templates** give control of the rendered areas, although mistakes can easily be rectified using a putty rubber. Once applied, chalk pastels should be **'fixed'** to the paper otherwise they will smudge if handled.

Your teacher will help you select a suitable subject for pastel rendering. In this example, a table lamp has been designed and rendered.

WORKED EXAMPLE

The task is to design a desk lamp using geometric forms such as cylinders, spheres, cones, pyramids and prisms. The designer should also consider combining different materials such as wood, metal and plastic.

1. Sketch design ideas.

- Use pencil and coloured pencils to design a lamp from geometric forms.
- Begin with 2-D sketches and develop your ideas in pictorial form.
- Quickly render them using coloured pencil – this is good practice and helps to give you a feel for the forms that you will render in pastel.
- You can also experiment with layouts at this stage.

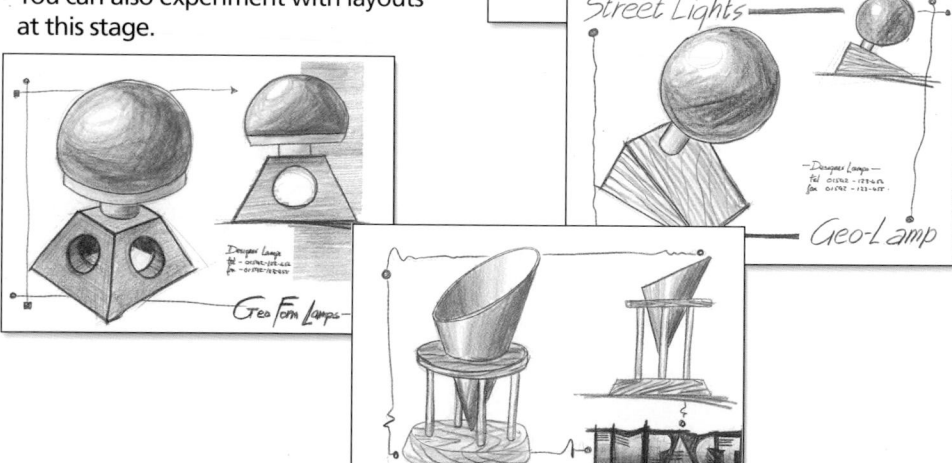

2. Prepare templates.

- Draw your chosen design carefully using instruments or a CAD package.
- Copy this drawing several times. It can be photocopied or printed from the computer.
- Use a craft knife, compass cutter, cutting mat and safety rule to expose different areas for application of different colours and tones.

3. Prepare work area.

- Cover your work area with newspaper to protect the work table.

4. Lubricate drawing sheet.

- Lubricate your drawing sheet by rubbing in some talcum powder with a cotton wool ball. This helps to produce an 'even' tone when the pastel is applied.

5. Powderise pastels.

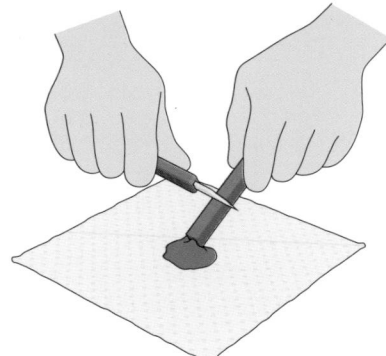

- Select a pastel stick and use a craft knife to scrape powder onto a paper towel.

CHALK PASTELS – LAYOUT AND DISPLAY

6. Fix template over drawing sheet.

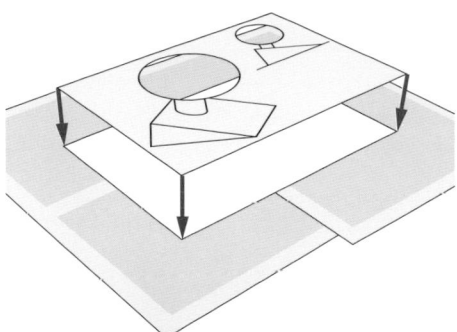

- Align a template sheet with the drawing sheet. Make sure they cannot move as you work. Low-tack masking tape will help keep the template in place.

7. Apply pastel powder.

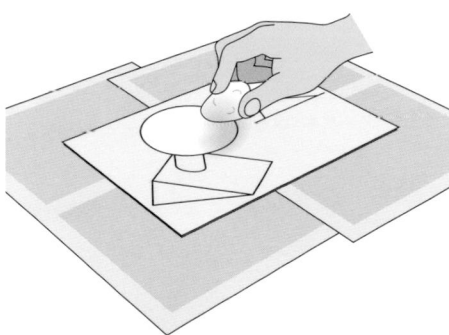

- Apply pastels by picking up some powder using cotton wool or cotton buds and rubbing onto the drawing sheet to produce a tonal effect.
- When applying each pastel, work from the dark tones towards the highlight. Ease the pressure as you go.
- Practise this technique before you begin your illustration.

8. Repeat for each template.

- Repeat stages 6 and 7 for each template sheet.
- Neatness and accuracy here provide evidence of good draughtmanship.

TIPS

- Try to prevent the pastel powder from **creeping** under the cut edges of the template sheets. You can achieve this by starting your strokes on the template and moving onto the drawing sheet. This will result in clean, sharp edges which require very little correction.
- Use a putty rubber to make any corrections.

9. Fix pastels.

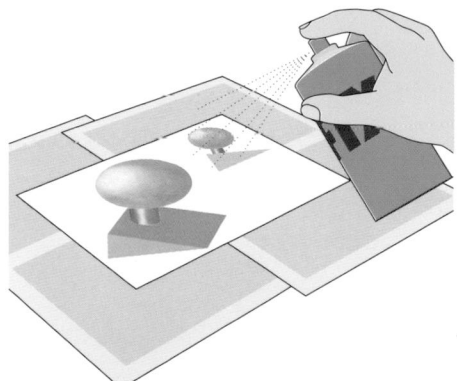

- Fix pastels with fixative spray or a cheap, non-scented hairspray. Use the spray in a well ventilated area.

10. Add detail.

- Use coloured pencils to detail the wood grain and shadow on the base.

11. Cut and paste your illustration.

- Use a craft knife, safety rule, cutting mat and scissors to cut out your illustrations.
- Carefully paste them onto your backdrop.

12. Evaluation of the layout and display.

- The black lines and text are created on the computer and printed on a strong red paper.
- The effect is very formal and geometric.
- The large lamp dominates the display because it is the only pictorial image.
- The position of the large lamp on top of the black line gives depth to the display, as does the presence of the small lamp.
- The use of green and red creates a strong, eye-catching contrast.

PORTFOLIO ASSESSMENT VALUES			
Topic	**Grade**	**Topic**	**Grade**
Graphs & Charts		Modelling	
Use of Colour	1	CAD	
Toning & Rendering	1	CAD Library	
Layout & Lettering	1	CAG Display	
Display	1	Draughtsmanship	1

MODELLING – RESEARCH AND DESIGN

INTRODUCTION

In the modelling part of the course you must make a 3-D card model. To be sure of gaining a Credit level grade 1, your model must be a complex item with surface detail (graphics). The quality of work (drawing, cutting, assembly and surface graphics) must also be of a high standard.

Your teacher may give you a design brief to get you started. If you are writing your own design brief, point-of-sale displays (like the following worked example), packaging and product storage are useful starting points. Products such as golf balls, mini-skateboards ('fingerboards'), cosmetics and aerosol toiletry sprays are easy to find and are of suitable sizes for this project.

TIPS

- Obtain a sample of the product you are going to display.
- Make sure that you are familiar with the geometric drawing skills (including surface developments and true shapes) found on pages 12 to 16. You will need these skills in this topic.

HOMEWORK TASK

The packaging around a product has several functions. State three functions of packaging.

WORKED EXAMPLE

Design brief

You are to create a point-of-sale display for a deodorant spray atomiser, 'FUJI', a new deodorant product for teenagers. The design should display the product to good effect and use company colour schemes and logos.

The cosmetics company requires a card model of your proposed solution.

1. Sketch your design ideas.

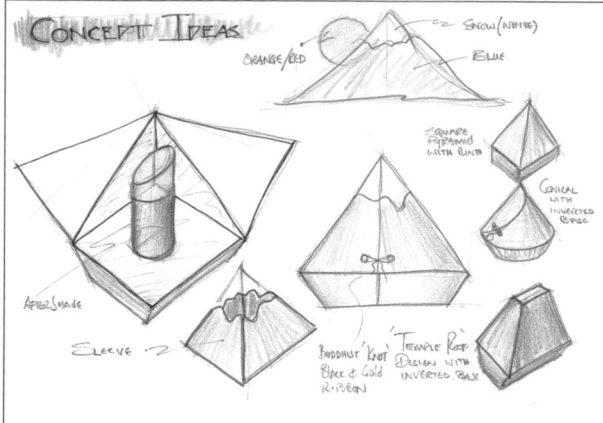

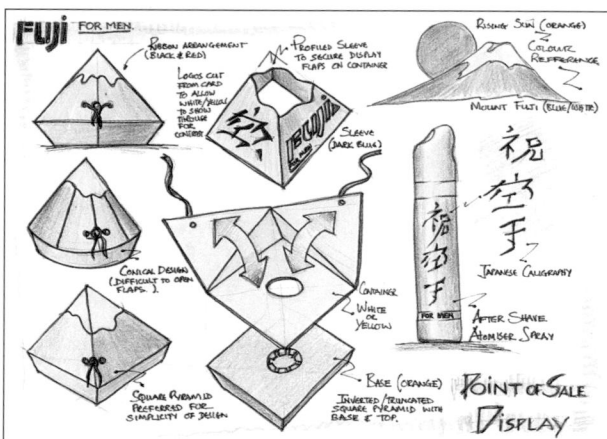

- Sketch out design ideas in pencil.
- Experiment with geometric forms, e.g. cones, cylinders, pyramids and prisms.
- Combine two or more geometric forms to create a complex form.
- Further complexity can be introduced by using hidden inserts, windows, etc.
- Remember that you must model your chosen design in card, so take advice from your teacher at this stage.

2. Sketch developments for main components.

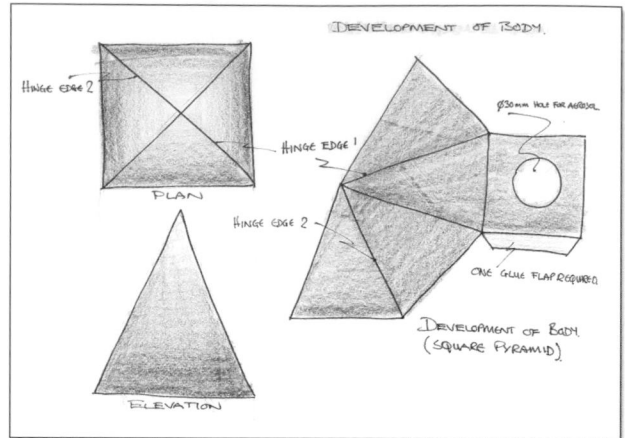

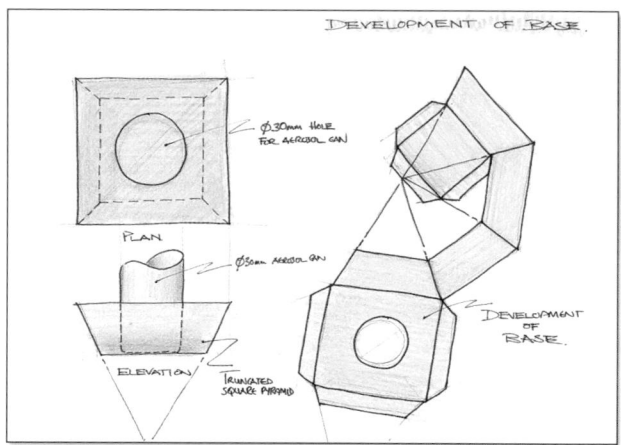

- Sketch two orthographic views of your main components. (In this example, an elevation and plan of the two main parts are shown.)
- Sketch the surface development of each component. This can be difficult – seek advice from your teacher if you need it. Add glue tabs to the model as required.
- It is useful to make these sketches before you tackle accurate drawings – sketching is quick and enables you to make design modifications.

MODELLING – PRODUCTION DRAWINGS AND MANUFACTURE

3. Sketch ideas for colour scheme, text and logo.

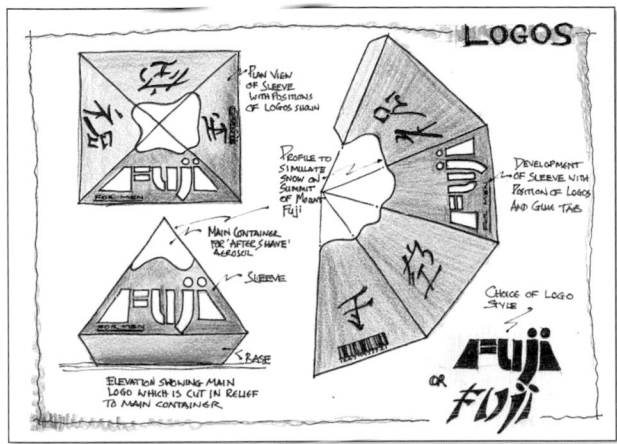

- Sketch out design ideas for colour schemes.
- In this example, a theme has been used: the package represents Mount Fuji in Japan and features a snow cap and Japanese-style text.

4. Draw accurate production drawings.

In this example, the production drawing below shows the elevation and plan of the model and the surface development for the body. The production drawing on the right shows the surface developments for the base and sleeve.

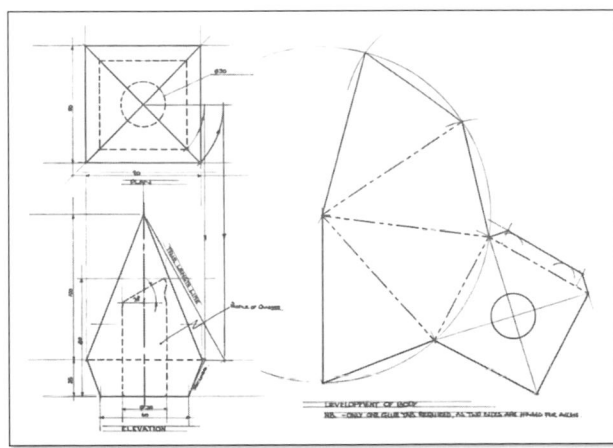

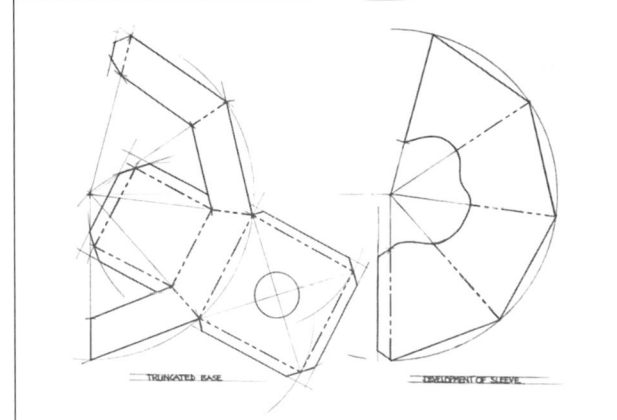

- These drawings can either be made on paper first and then transferred to card or drawn directly on to card.
- Draw at least two orthographic views. In this example, the elevation and plan of each part have been drawn to a 1:1 scale.
- If you are displaying or storing a product, draw the product first. The package is then drawn around the product.
- Draw a surface development of each part. Include glue tabs and fold lines.
- Add colour, text and logo before the developments have been cut out. It is much easier at this stage.

5. Cutting, folding and fixing.
- Carefully cut out the surface developments. Use a safety rule, cutting mat and craft knife.
- Score along the fold lines to give a neat, sharp edge.
- Glue and assemble the model.
- Neatness and accuracy throughout each step provide evidence of good draughtmanship.

PORTFOLIO ASSESSMENT VALUES

Topic	Grade	Topic	Grade
Graphs & Charts		Modelling	1
Use of Colour		CAD	
Toning & Rendering		CAD Library	
Layout & Lettering		CAG Display	
Display		Draughtsmanship	1

6. Photograph the model.
A photograph of your model may be taken if your portfolio has to be sent to the SQA for moderation.

COMPUTER-AIDED DRAWING – ORTHOGRAPHIC CAD

INTRODUCTION

During your course you will produce one orthographic and one pictorial drawing using a computer-aided drawing (CAD) software package. The worked examples shown on pages 66 to 69 are typical Credit level drawings.

There are many CAD software packages available today. You may use a different package from the one used here, but the basic principles are the same and the drawing tools and functions will be similar.

In this first worked example, two views of a personal CD player are drawn in orthographic projection. These drawings have been copied from a worksheet provided by the teacher but you can measure and draw from a real product if you wish. Do **not** include in your portfolio any drawings that are produced using a step-by-step guide.

The purpose of this worked example is to explain:
• the main steps in constructing CAD drawings
• when to use CAD tools and functions such as layers
• what standard of drawing is required to achieve Credit level.

MORE INFO

At Credit level you must produce drawings which include:
• a complex object or building
• at least two related views
• hidden detail
• centre lines
• detailed dimensions (Ø, R and linear)
• descriptive text
• a projection symbol
• a high degree of accuracy.

LAYERS

The example shown has been constructed on several layers. Centre lines, construction lines, outlines and dimensions are all drawn on separate layers. This makes CAD drawing simpler.

The construction layer can be hidden when the CAD drawing is complete – this makes the drawing easier to understand.

You should use layers when constructing your own CAD drawing.

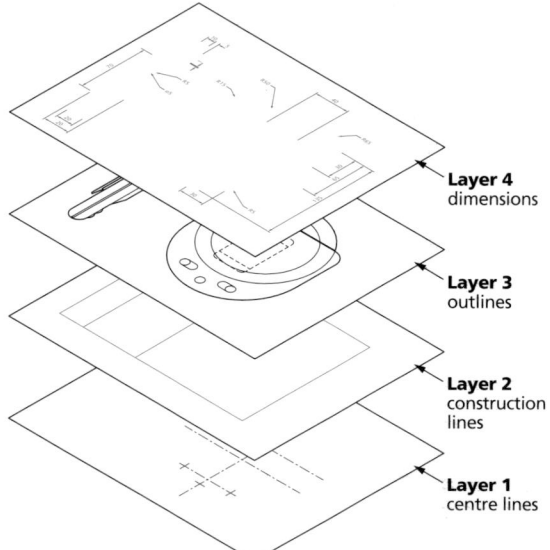

Layer 4
dimensions

Layer 3
outlines

Layer 2
construction
lines

Layer 1
centre lines

WORKED EXAMPLE

1. Draw the construction lines.
• Set **GRID** size 10 mm, **SNAP** size 5 mm.
• Set **ORTHO**.
• Select **LAYER 1**.
• Draw centre lines.
• Select **LAYER 2**.
• Construct a box for the elevation.
• **EXTEND** horizontal lines and construct a box for the end elevation.
• Use **SAVE AS** to name and save your drawing.

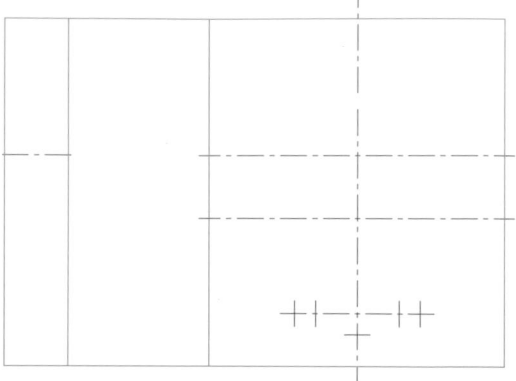

2. Draw the elevation.
• Select **LAYER 3**.
• Draw the two large circles using the **CIRCLE** tool.
• **ZOOM IN** and draw the right-hand slide button (see the tip box below).
• **GROUP** all parts of the slide button.
• **ZOOM OUT**.
• **MIRROR/REFLECT** the slide button to produce the left-hand button.
• Draw the centre button using the **CIRCLE** tool.
• **SAVE** your drawing.

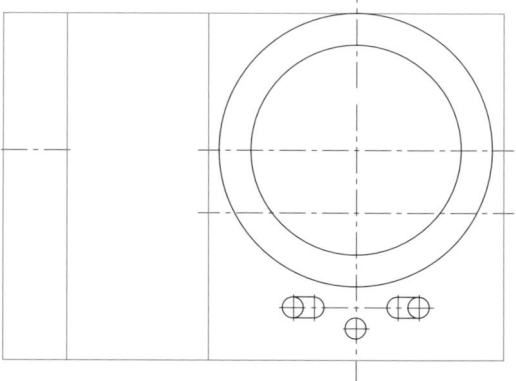

TIP

Use this method for drawing a slide button:

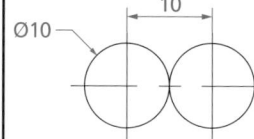

• Draw centre lines and two Ø10 circles.

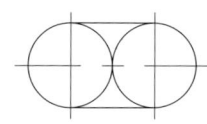

• Join circles with two horizontal tangent lines.

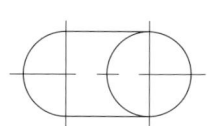

• Select left-hand circle and use **BREAK** to remove half the circle.

3. Complete the elevation.

- Draw a **CIRCLE** and **BREAK** the top half to create the bottom curve.
- Draw a **LINE** at the top and the sides.
- Set the **FILLET** radius to R15 and **FILLET** the two corners near the top.
- **SAVE** your drawing.

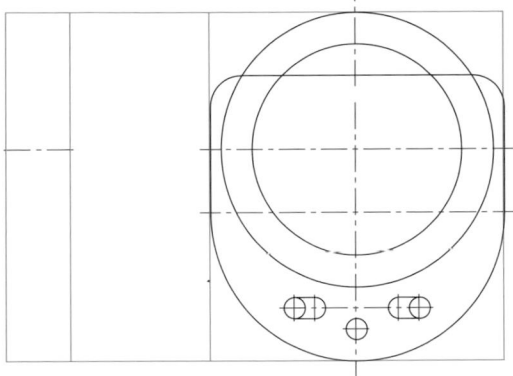

4. Draw the end elevation.

- Select **LAYER 2**.
- Project outline details across to the end elevation.
- Select **LAYER 3**.
- Set **SNAP** to 2 mm.
- **ZOOM IN** and use **FILLET** to round the corners on both views.
- **ZOOM OUT**.
- **SAVE** your drawing.

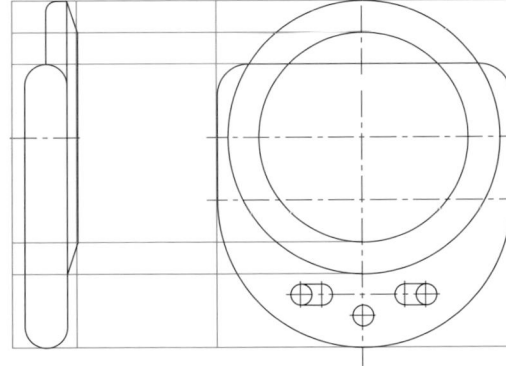

5. Add details.

- **ZOOM IN** and add details: headphone socket, belt clip and break lines. (Break lines are where two separate parts of an injection-moulded casing join together.)
- **ZOOM OUT**.
- Add hidden detail to show the belt clip on the **ELEVATION**.
- **SAVE** your drawing.

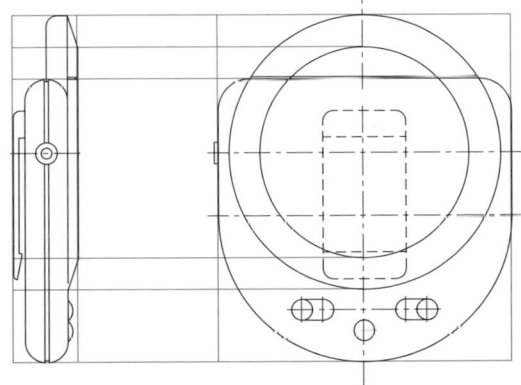

6. Add dimensions and text.

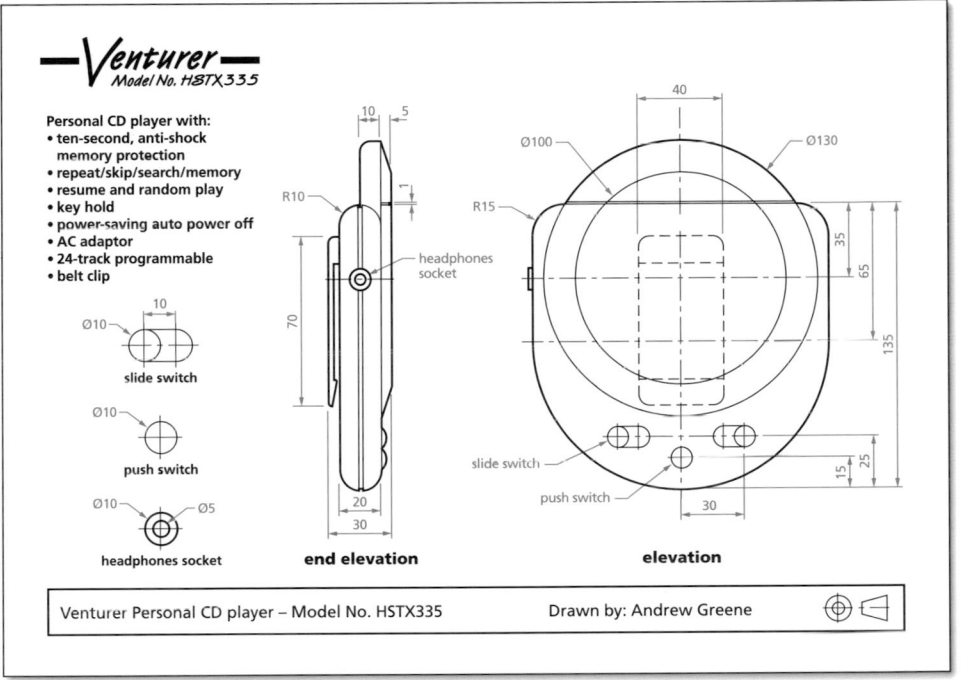

- Select **LAYER 4**.
- Add dimensions (the software uses **auto-dimensioning** to calculate the measurements itself).
- Add descriptive text and a projection symbol.
- Using commands **EDIT** and **CHANGE PROPERTIES**, increase **LINE THICKNESS** to thicken the outlines of the drawing.
- Hide **LAYER 2** to hide construction lines.
- **SAVE** and **PRINT** your drawing. The drawing is known as a **hard copy** when printed on paper.
- The correct use of British Standards conventions and symbols, as well as neatness and accuracy, provides evidence of good draughtsmanship.

PORTFOLIO ASSESSMENT VALUES			
Topic	**Grade**	**Topic**	**Grade**
Graphs & Charts		Modelling	
Use of Colour		CAD	1
Toning & Rendering		CAD Library	
Layout & Lettering		CAG Display	
Display		Draughtsmanship	1

COMPUTER-AIDED DRAWING – PICTORIAL CAD

INTRODUCTION

The second computer-aided drawing in your portfolio is a pictorial drawing. You can draw virtually anything but it is helpful if you can also make use of this drawing in another graphic – for example, the CAD drawing of a house produced here is also used in the bar chart shown on page 55. Incorporating your pictorial CAD drawing into another topic, such as Graphs and Charts or CAG for Display, will save you time which you can then use to improve the quality of your portfolio (see page 51).

At Credit level you must produce a pictorial drawing of a complex object or building. The drawing must demonstrate a high degree of accuracy and neatness.

Choose your subject carefully. A building is normally constructed with straight lines – this can make it easier to draw than objects which include lots of curves. The drawing in this example is constructed entirely of straight lines, but it is complex, detailed and neatly drawn so will be assessed at Credit level, grade 1. This example is not produced to scale – sizes are not as important as proportion and perspective.

TIPS

- Construct the drawing on layers.
- Select layer 1 when drawing construction lines.
- Select layer 2 when drawing outlines.

WORKED EXAMPLE

1. Choose the most suitable style of drawing for your subject.

- Your drawing can be isometric, oblique, planometric or perspective. Two-point perspective has been chosen here because it is the most realistic style.
- Always sketch or draw your chosen subject first. This helps to give you a feel for the style of drawing.
- The CAD drawing produced in this example is based on the freehand sketch of a house shown on the right. The CAD drawing will later be used to enhance a bar chart about house prices.

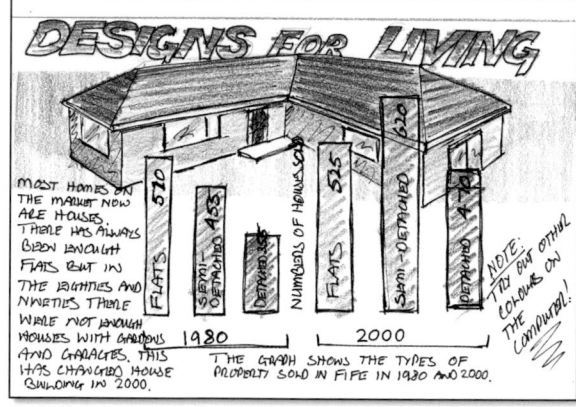

2. Set out the drawing.

- Use **GRID** and **SNAP** to keep the corners neat.
- Draw a horizon line and two vanishing points (VPs).
- Draw the two front vertical edges and project the tops and bottoms back to the VPs.
- Draw the other vertical edges. Remove **SNAP** and use **TRIM** to reduce the heights.

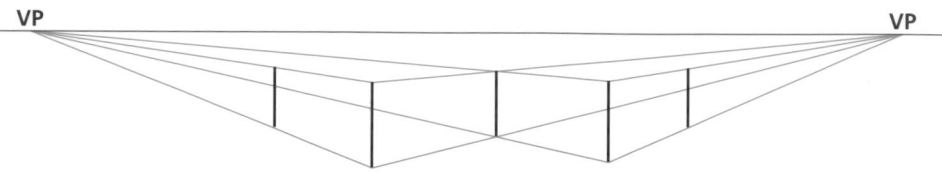

TIP

Beyond this stage, perspective drawing requires that you work without **SNAP**. Your CAD software will have another function called **ATTACH** (or **JOIN**) which keeps corners neat and accurate. Work with **ATTACH** on when you need to join a line to a corner or to the end of another line.

3. Add the roof lines.

- Use the vanishing points to obtain good perspective.

The grade for the drawing at this stage is General level, grade 4.

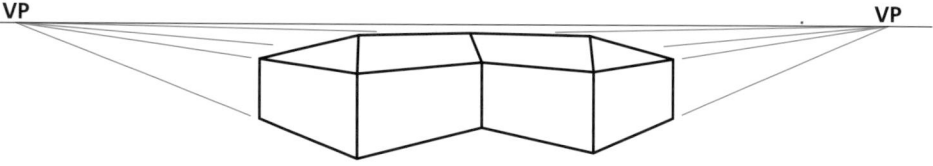

4. Add windows and door.

- Draw the front vertical edges and project lines from the tops and bottoms back to the VPs.
- Draw the other vertical edges.
- The house is not drawn to scale so sizes do not matter. However, getting the proportions and perspective correct is essential.

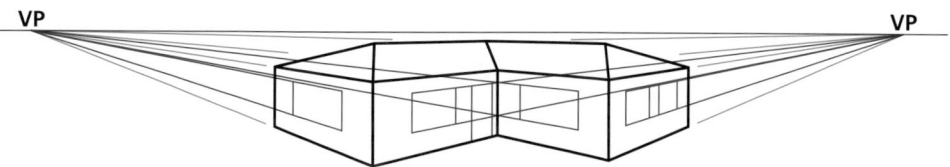

5. Hide the construction lines to make the drawing clearer and easier to work on.

• Hiding **LAYER 1** will do this. You can view them again when you need to.

The grade for the drawing at this stage is General level, grade 3.

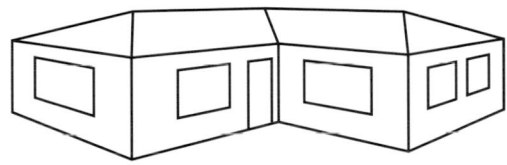

6. To gain a Credit level grade 1, add more detail and complexity.

• The eaves of most houses stick out past the walls. **EXTEND** the sloping roof lines out past the walls (**1**).
• **COPY** and **MOVE** the lines at the eaves to give depth to the eaves (**2**).
• Use **COPY** on the window and door lines to create the thickness going into the walls (**3**).
• **ZOOM IN** to **TRIM** lines and close gaps.
• Add extra details such as steps, a chimney, a garage or a patio to give your drawing complexity.

The drawing at this stage has the complexity and quality to gain a Credit level, grade 1.

PORTFOLIO ASSESSMENT VALUES			
Topic	**Grade**	**Topic**	**Grade**
Graphs & Charts		Modelling	
Use of Colour		CAD	1
Toning & Rendering		CAD Library	
Layout & Lettering		CAG Display	
Display		Draughtsmanship	1

ENHANCING YOUR PICTORIAL CAD DRAWING

You may want to enhance your CAD drawing by rendering it in colour. You will not gain any extra credit for this in your CAD assessments, but it could make the drawing more suitable for use in another portfolio piece. Also, producing a CAG illustration will be a useful experience if you intend to progress to Intermediate 2 or Higher, where CAG illustration is compulsory.

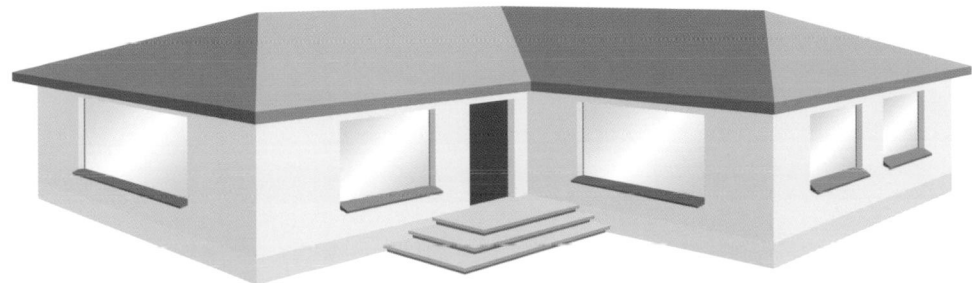

• **EXPORT** your CAD line drawing to an illustration programme such as Designworks or CorelDRAW.
• Trace over each area to add colour (the **AUTO-TRACE** command speeds this up).
• **ZOOM IN** and tidy up corners and edges.
• Add a cylindrical **FILL STYLE** to show reflections in the glass.
• Adjust the tones on the roof and walls to suggest a light source.

A drawing like this takes about an hour to render. This example has been rendered for use in the bar chart shown here. This bar chart can be assessed in several topics. (See pages 51 and 55 for more information.)

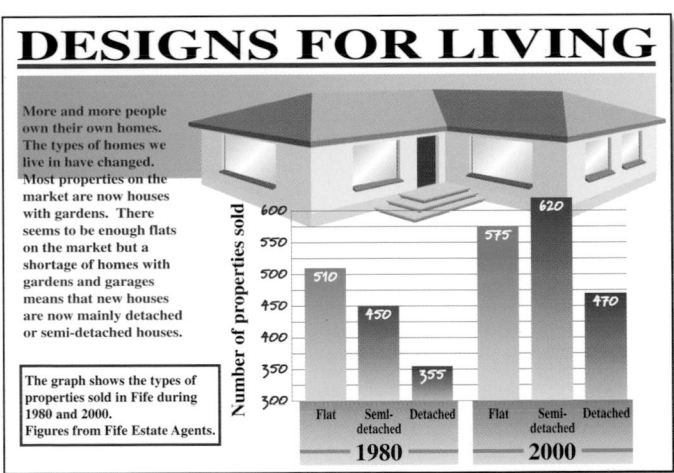

DESIGNS FOR LIVING

More and more people own their own homes. The types of homes we live in have changed. Most properties on the market are now houses with gardens. There seems to be enough flats on the market but a shortage of homes with gardens and garages means that new houses are now mainly detached or semi-detached houses.

The graph shows the types of properties sold in Fife during 1980 and 2000. Figures from Fife Estate Agents.

USING A CAD LIBRARY

INTRODUCTION

Architects and designers produce thousands of computer-aided drawings. Many of these drawings have identical parts. Drawing a new part each time would be repetitive and time-consuming. The solution is to use a **CAD library** of common or standard parts.

For example, a firm of architects who specialise in designing large hotels will draw floor plans that include hundreds of doors and windows and perhaps thousands of sockets, switches and light fittings. One drawing of each part is made; these drawings are known as **icons**. Each icon is then saved as a **part file** and stored in a **CAD library folder**. When an icon is required, it is simply brought from the CAD library and placed onto the drawing. This can be done as often as is required. Because the finished drawing is built up using library parts, it is known as a **composite** drawing.

> **TIP**
>
> Remember, the computing terms 'folder' and 'directory' mean the same thing. Refer back to page 45 if you are unsure about any of the computing terms used here.

The advantages of using a CAD library are that it:
• saves drawing time by storing standard components and parts
• can be added to and modified over a period of time to keep up with new designs.

ASSESSMENT

The assessment for this topic depends not only on the quality of the finished drawing but also on the degree to which you have used the CAD library.

• At Foundation level, you need only select icons from a CAD library and place them on a drawing.
• At General level, you must also manipulate (rotate, scale or mirror) the icons.
• To gain Credit level you must create your own library folder and create icons that you save as part files. These are then recalled from your library and used in a composite drawing.

Note that these procedures are not evident from your drawing, so you must state exactly what you did to produce the drawing. (See the finished example on page 71.)

OTHER TOPICS FOR CAD LIBRARY DRAWINGS

Floor plans and building drawings are obvious examples of the types of drawings where a CAD library is useful. When producing your own CAD library drawing it can be fun to explore other ideas. Here are some examples to help you to get started:
• yacht marina
• go-kart track
• airport
• fishing harbour
• golf course
• cafeteria
• garden and patio design
• play park
• housing estate
• railway station.

EXAMPLE CAD LIBRARY DRAWINGS

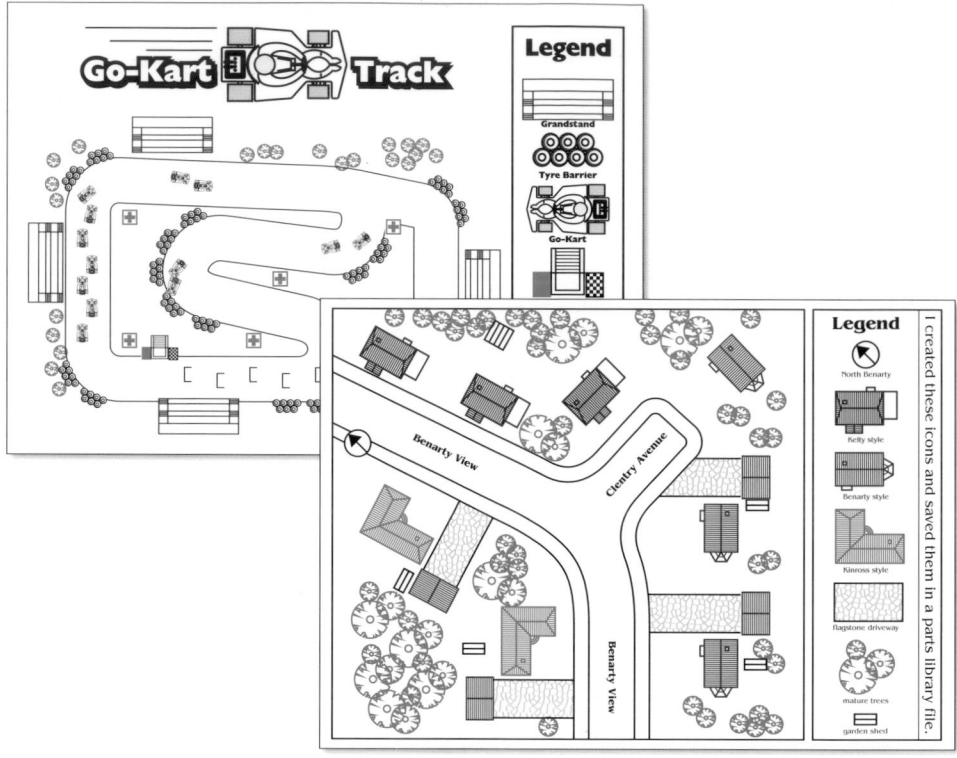

WORKED EXAMPLE

Design and draw your ideal bedroom. You can redesign your own bedroom or start from scratch and design an entirely new layout.

1. Draw your design in pencil on squared paper.

• This helps you design the layout and contents of the room without wasting valuable computer time.
• Your teacher may require you to draw to a scale. If you are using A3 paper, a 1:20 scale is normally suitable for bedroom floor plans. Measuring your own bedroom at home will help you plan the dimensions.
• Refer to the floor plans on page 33 for more information.

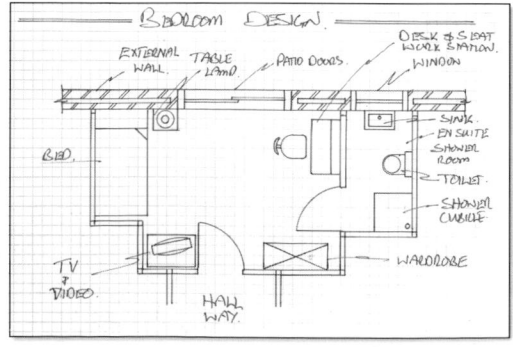

2. Create a CAD library folder.

- This can be done by creating a new folder called 'bedroom' in your CAD files folder.
- If your CAD software already has its own library folder (called 'parts'), create your library folder within that instead.

Your teacher will explain this and may even have the library folder prepared for you. It is important to remember that the procedure you use for creating a library folder will vary depending on the computer system you are using and on your teacher's preference.

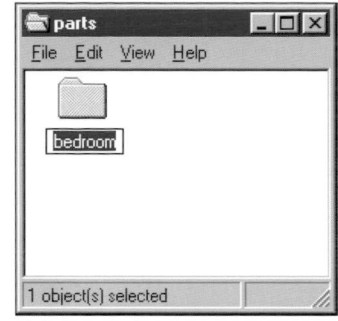

3. Draw the walls, windows and doors of your bedroom.

- Set up an A3 page and set the **SHEET SCALE** to 1:20.
- Set **GRID** and **SNAP** to an appropriate size – this will depend on your pencil drawing.
- Draw the outlines accurately.
- Show which way the doors open.
- If required, each part can be saved in the library later. In this example, however, only the contents of the bedroom will be saved in the library.

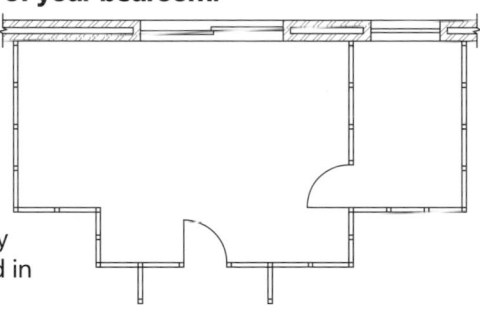

4. Draw and save each icon in your library folder.

- Draw the bed. Your teacher may provide you with examples of standard symbols to copy or you can design your own.
- **GROUP** all the lines on the icon to make it easier to manipulate.
- Open your bedroom parts library folder using the **PART CLIP** command.
- Save your bed icon as the file 'bed' in your bedroom library folder. A typical **PART CLIP** dialog box for saving parts is shown on the right.

5. Draw and save the remaining icons in your bedroom parts library.

- Each icon is drawn separately and saved in the bedroom library as a new part file.
- In this example, different colours have been used to distinguish the bedroom furniture from the en suite fittings.

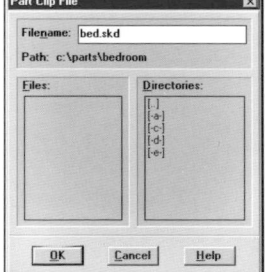

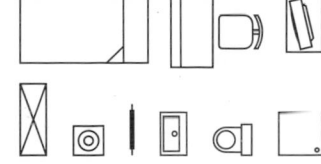

6. Complete the CAD library drawing.

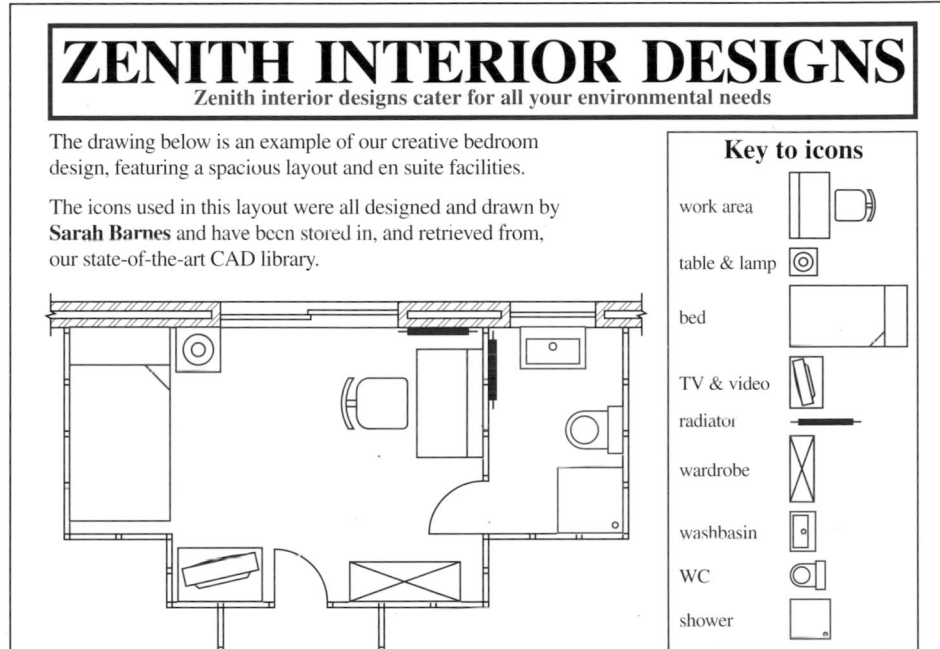

ZENITH INTERIOR DESIGNS
Zenith interior designs cater for all your environmental needs

The drawing below is an example of our creative bedroom design, featuring a spacious layout and en suite facilities.

The icons used in this layout were all designed and drawn by **Sarah Barnes** and have been stored in, and retrieved from, our state-of-the-art CAD library.

Key to icons

work area

table & lamp

bed

TV & video

radiator

wardrobe

washbasin

WC

shower

- Recall the icons from the CAD library. Your CAD software will enable you to view your bedroom library through a **PART INSERT** command. (See the screenshot on the right.)
- Manipulate (**ROTATE**, **SCALE** or **MIRROR**) the icons and position them carefully, avoiding overlaps with other drawing parts.
- Create a **key** (or **legend**) to identify the icons.
- State clearly on your drawing that you have created icons, stored them in a library file and recalled these icons to place them in the composite drawing.
- Finish off the piece by presenting it as an advertising graphic.
- Neatness and accuracy provide evidence of good draughtsmanship.

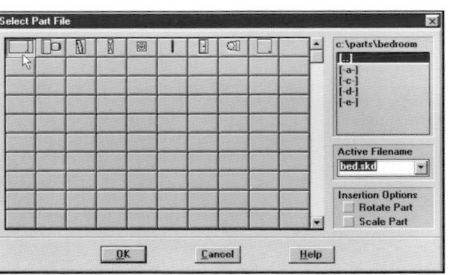

Topic	Grade	Topic	Grade
Graphs & Charts		Modelling	
Use of Colour		CAD	
Toning & Rendering		CAD Library	1
Layout & Lettering		CAG Display	
Display		Draughtsmanship	1

PORTFOLIO ASSESSMENT VALUES

ANSWERS TO HOMEWORK TASKS

Page 6, Task 1
1. 4
2. barrel and shaft
3. shaft
4. Ø8
5. 7

Page 6, Task 2
1. metric thread Ø6
2. barrel
3. barrel
4. centre line, cutting plane and fold line
5. surface development of flights

Page 33

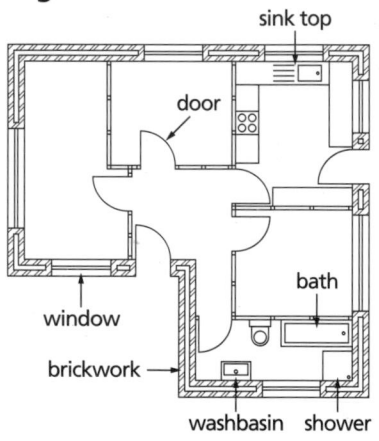

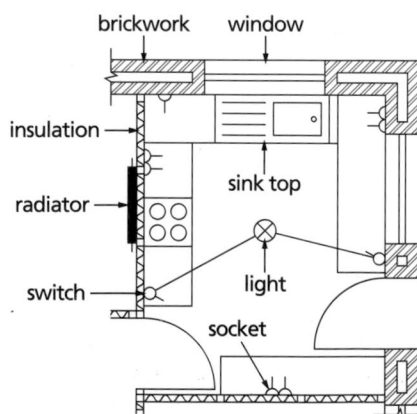

Page 34
1. radiator, in-line valve, crossover, junction (see diagram below)

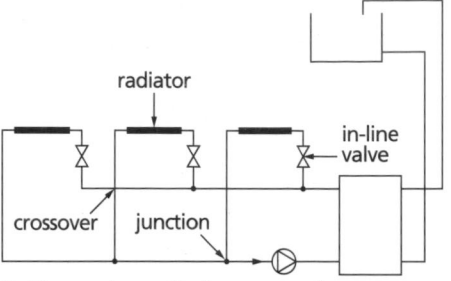

2. The water splits into two pipes, or comes together into one pipe.
3. The arrow indicates the direction in which water flows through the pump.

Page 35, Rail Network
1. Paisley Canal, Central
2. 4 (including Kilwinning and Troon)
3. St Enoch, Buchanan St, Cowcaddens, St George's Cross, Kelvinbridge, Hillhead, Kelvinhall, Partick, Govan, Ibrox, Cessnock, Kinning Park, Shields Rd, West St, Bridge St (any 3)
4. Hillington West, Central
5. Underground Network

Page 35, Kitchen Base Unit
1. B – Left Hand End, H – Plinth, F – Back Rail
2. Wood Dowel, Cross-axial Screw
3. 12
4. 90° hinge, opens door to 90°
5. 10

Page 36
Ask your teacher to check your answers.

Page 37

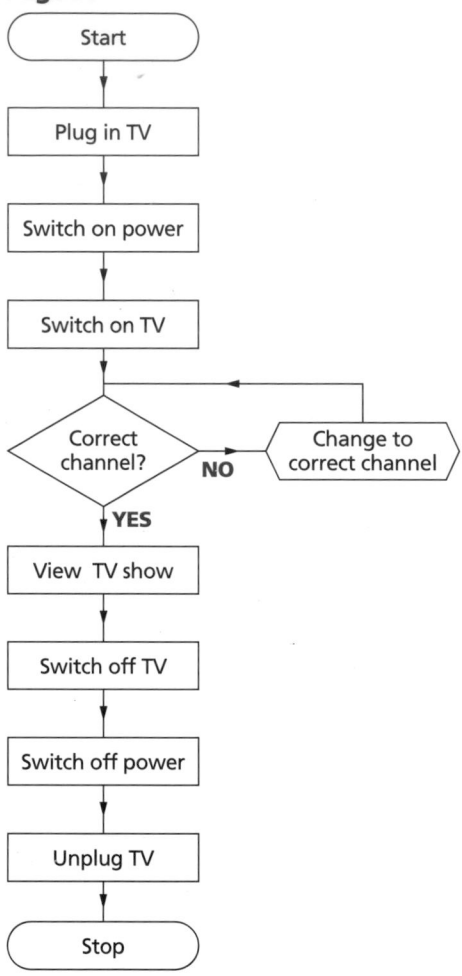

(Note: your flow chart may be more complex than the one shown here, depending on the number of stages you include.)

Page 38

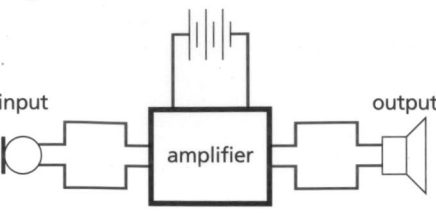

Page 39
Ask your teacher to check your answers.

Page 41
The left-hand graphic uses three equally-spaced colours to make an exciting colour scheme. The right-hand graphic uses colours near each other to make a harmonious colour scheme.

Page 42
Ask your teacher to check your answers.

Page 52
Ask your teacher to check your answers.

Page 47, Task 1
1. modem
2. drum plotter
3. ink-jet printer or colour laser printer

Page 47, Task 2
1. as insurance against files being lost
2. scanner
3. hard drive, floppy disc, Zip disc, CD-R, DVD (any 4)

Page 64
to protect the product; to display information about the product; to advertise the product; to enable stacking, storage or display (any 3)